The Awful Disclosures of
MARIA MONK

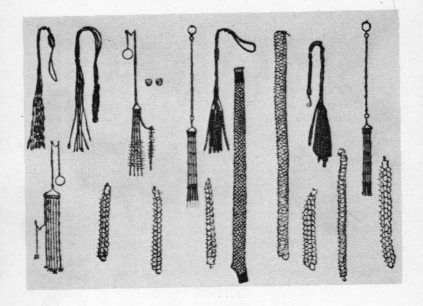

Articles of Piety

Torture and mortification instruments were still being used in English convents after the Maria Monk era. Michelet's *Priests, Women, and Families* illustrates the above and other objects, some for "the most cruel and immodest purposes." All were made of iron. Little's Ecclesiastical Warehouse, in London, at 20 Cranbourne Street, was supplying Hair-shirts at 12s. 6d. in 1869, a Massive Waist Chain at 8s. 6d., and a 9-tail Discipline at 6s. 6d.

The Awful Disclosures of
MARIA MONK

The hidden secrets of convent life

Together with
THE CARDIERE CASE

SENATE

The Awful Disclosures of Maria Monk
and *The Cardiere Case*

Previously published in a single volume paperback
in 1969 by Canova Press Ltd, London

This paperback edition published in 1997 by Senate,
an imprint of Random House UK Ltd, Random House,
20 Vauxhall Bridge Road, London SW1V 2SA.

ISBN 1 85958 499 3

Printed and bound in Great Britain by
Cox & Wyman, Reading, Berkshire

CONTENTS

Maria Monk

	Page
Introduction	XI
Preface	XV

CHAPTER I

Early recollections – Early life – Religious education neglected – First school – Entrance into the school of the Congregational Nunnery – Brief account of the Nunneries in Montreal – The Congregational Nunnery – The Black Nunnery – The Grey Nunnery – Public respect for these institutions – Instructions received – The Catechism – The Bible

1

CHAPTER II

Congregational Nunnery – Story told by fellow-pupil against a priest – Other stories – Pretty Mary – Confession to Father Richards – My subsequent confession – Instructions in the Catechism

6

CHAPTER III

Black Nunnery – Preparations to become a novice in the Black Nunnery – Entrance – Occupations of the novices – The apartments to which they had access – First interview with Jane Ray – Reverence for the Superior – A wonderful nun – Her reliques – The holy good shepherd, or nameless nun – Confession of novices

9

Page

CHAPTER IV

Displeased with the Convent – Left it – Residence at St. Denis – Relics – Marriage – Return to the Black Nunnery – Objections made by some novices   16

CHAPTER V

Received confirmation – Painful feelings – Specimens of instructions received on the subject   20

CHAPTER VI

Taking the veil – Interview afterwards with the Superior – Surprise and horror at the disclosures – Resolution to submit   22

CHAPTER VII

Daily ceremonies – Jane Ray among the nuns   29

CHAPTER VIII

Description of apartments in the Black Nunnery, in order: 1st floor – 2nd floor – Garret – The founder – Superior's management with the friends of novices – Religious lies – criminality of concealing sins at confession   35

CHAPTER IX

Nuns with similar names – Squaw nuns – First visit to the cellar – Description of it – Shocking discovery there – Superior's instructions – Private signal of the priests – Books used in the Nunnery – Opinions expressed of the Bible – Specimens of what I know of the Scriptures   46

Page

CHAPTER X

Manufacture of bread and wax candles, carried on in the Convent – Superstitions – Scapularies – Virgin Mary's pincushion – Her house – The Bishop's power over fire – My instructions to novices – Jane Ray – Vacillation of feelings

52

CHAPTER XI

Alarming order from the Superior – Proceed to execute it – Scene in an upper room – Sentence of death, and murder – My own distress – Reports made to friends of St. Frances

59

CHAPTER XII

Description of the room of the Three States, and the pictures in it – Jane Ray – Ridiculing priests – Their criminal treatment of us at confession – Jane Ray's tricks with the nuns' aprons, handkerchiefs, and nightgowns – Apples

65

CHAPTER XIII

Jane Ray's tricks continued – The broomstick ghost – Sleep-walking –Salted cider – Changing beds – Objects of some of her tricks – Feigned humility – Alarm

72

CHAPTER XIV

Influencing novices – Difficulty of convincing persons from the United States – Tale of the Bishop in the city – The Bishop in the Convent – The prisoners in the cells – Practice in singing – Narratives – Jane Ray's hymns – The Superior's best trick

86

CHAPTER XV

Frequency of the priests' visits to the Nunnery – Their
freedom and crimes – Difficulty of learning their names
– Their holy retreat – Objections in our minds – Means
used to counteract conscience – Ingenious arguments   94

CHAPTER XVI

Treatments of young infants in the Convent – Talking
in sleep – Amusements – Ceremonies at the public inter-
ment of deceased nuns – Sudden disappearance of the old
Superior – Introduction of the new one – Superstition
– Alarm of a nun – Difficulty of communication with other
nuns   99

CHAPTER XVII

Disappearance of nuns – St. Pierre – Gags – My temporary confinement in a cell – The cholera season – How
to avoid it – Occupations in the Convent during the pesti-
ence – Manufacture of wax candles – The election
riots – Alarm among the nuns – Preparations for defence
– Penances   105

CHAPTER XVIII

The punishment of the cap – The priests of the district
of Montreal have free access to the Black Nunnery –
Crimes committed and required by them – The Pope's
command to commit indecent crimes – Characters of the
old and new Superiors – The timidity of the latter – I
began to be employed in the hospitals – Some account of
them – Warning given me by a sick nun – Penance of
hanging   117

CHAPTER XIX

More visits to the imprisoned nuns – Their fears – Others
temporarily put into the cells – Relics – The Agnus Dei
– The priests' private hospital, or holy retreat – Secret
rooms in the eastern wing – Reports of murders in the
Convent – The Superior's private records – Number of
nuns in the Convent – Desire of escape – Urgent reason for
it – Plan – Deliberation – Attempt – Success   123

Conclusion   132

The Cadiere Case

Page 139

INTRODUCTION

NOTHING attracts the public attention or fires the collective imagination more strongly than works which unmask and reveal the iniquities which are sometimes practised beneath the protective cloak of religion. It is not, however, difficult to comprehend why this should be so. The alliance of the two most powerful and seemingly contradictory urges in mankind – the spiritual and the fleshly – is irresistible. For a time the pull of these opposed impulses, which are present to a greater or lesser degree in all men and women, is resolved. At the same time, a third appetite is satisfied – that of vicarious justification.

The majority of men and women are not saints and do not aspire or profess so to be, yet the spiritual impulse, thanks to the power of the established churches and the moral teachings of society persists as guilt and doubt. There is no better way of assuaging this guilt and, incidentally, little besides that men so much enjoy, than to discover that holy institutions and their righteous inmates also share in the imperfections and urges for which they constantly berate the general populace. Disclosures of the kind contained in these pages re-affirm, albeit in a limited sphere, that all men are equal, that even the good are not always beyond reproach, that impulses which, though pleasurable, are pronounced wrong are the common heritage of all men, whether they be saints or sinners.

Herein lies the secret of the perpetual success of Maria Monk's *Awful Disclosures*. For over a hundred and thirty years,* Miss Monk's exposé of the conditions which obtained in the Hotel Dieu Nunnery during her brief but terrifying

* The text of the present version is taken from a very early edition published by T. B. Peterson of Philadelphia, and is thus quite authentic.

stay in that supposedly devout religious house, has been constantly in demand. Each succeeding generation has read her account of evil practices within the nunnery walls with excitement and absorbed interest, with the result that Maria Monk and her book have passed into the annals of literary legend. This amazing but deserved popularity proves conclusively and again that truth is stranger and more enduring than fiction.

In these days of widespread agnosticism, Maria Monk's revelations are necessarily less shocking than when they were first published. At that time, such a concerted, reasoned and honest account of the life behind the veil was bound to be greeted with horror and outrage. Thus, its authorship and publication must now be regarded as acts of considerable courage. Not surprising, the book was greeted with a torrent of abuse. The Catholic press, and sections of opinion with less obviously vested interests, were unanimous in their condemnation and refutation of Maria Monk's account of her experiences. Anonymously printed handbills were handed out in New York denouncing the book and accusing its authoress of ungodly calumny. Correspondence raged in the press but the truth contained in this explosive book was unquestionably confirmed by this statement in the *Long Island Star*:*

'It should be stated, in addition, that the authoress of the book, Maria Monk, is in New York and stands ready to answer any questions, and submit to any inquiries put in a proper manner, and desires nothing so strongly as an opportunity to prove before a court the truth of her story.'

Furthermore, Maria Monk was able to corroborate her claims by producing reliable witnesses. This show of good faith effectively prevented the detractors from taking the matter further, and, over the years, Maria Monk's story has been freed from any suggestion of untruth.

In this particular, Maria Monk's reception parallels that of Catherine Cadiere, whose extraordinary experiences at

* February 29, 1836.

the hands of a Jesuit priest are also included in this volume. Miss Cadiere suffered as the result of her charges, which were unwillingly brought. Maria Monk benefited from a more enlightened climate and from the fact that the church was, at the time she published her book, already much weakened.

In 1730, however, when the Cadiere Case occurred, the church was an almost omnipotent power and Catherine Cadiere, misused and deluded as a result of her experiences, was no fit match for the might of a wily and unscrupulous clergy.

The Cadiere Case was a *cause célèbre*, one of the most widely discussed scandals of the eighteenth century. It has for years been neglected and the publication of its details in this volume is the first to appear in England during this century. It is an amazing mixture of lust and religion, and it remains to this day one of the most shocking and iniquitous examples of what happens when a body, such as the church, becomes too powerful and thus creates opportunities for evil men to prey upon the innocent placed in their spiritual care.

PREFACE

It is to be hoped that the reader of the ensuing narrative will not suppose that it is a fiction, or that the scenes and persons that I have delineated, had not a real existence. It is also desired, that the author of this volume may be regarded not as a voluntary participator in the very guilty transactions which are described; but receive sympathy for the trials which she has endured, and the peculiar situation in which her past experience, and escape from the power of the Superior of the Hotel Dieu Nunnery, at Montreal, and the snares of the Roman Priests in Canada, have left her.

My feelings are frequently distressed and agitated by the recollection of what I have passed through; and by night and day I have little peace of mind, and few periods of calm and pleasing reflection. Futurity also appears uncertain. I know not what reception this little work may meet with, and what will be the effect of its publication here or in Canada, among strangers, friends, or enemies. I have given the world the truth, so far as I have gone, on subjects of which I am told they are generally ignorant; and I feel perfect confidence, that any facts which may yet be discovered, will confirm my words whenever they can be obtained. Whoever shall explore the Hotel Dieu Nunnery at Montreal, will find unquestionable evidence that the descriptions of the interior of that edifice, given in this book, were furnished by one familiar with them; for whatever alterations may be attempted, there are changes which no mason or carpenter can make and effectually conceal; and therefore there must be plentiful evidence in that Institution of the truth of my description.

There are living witnesses, also, who ought to be made to speak, without fear of penances, tortures, and death, and possibly their testimony at some future time, may be added.

to confirm my statements. There are witnesses I should greatly rejoice to see at liberty; or rather there *were*. Are they living now? or will they be permitted to live after the Priests and Superiors have seen this book? Perhaps the wretched nuns in the cells have already suffered for my sake – perhaps Jane Ray has been silenced for ever, or will be murdered, before she has time to add her most important testimony to mine.

But speedy death, in relation only to this world, can be no great calamity to those who lead the life of a nun. The mere recollection of it always makes me miserable. It would distress the reader, should I repeat the dreams with which I am often terrified at night; for I sometimes fancy myself pursued by the worst enemies; frequently I seem as if again shut up in the Convent; often I imagine myself present at the repetition of the worst scenes that I have hinted at or described. Sometimes I stand by the secret place of inter-ment in the cellar; sometimes I think I can hear the shrieks of the helpless females in the hands of atrocious men; and sometimes almost seem actually to look again upon the calm and placid features of St. Frances, as she appeared when surrounded by her murderers.

I cannot banish the scenes and character of this book from my memory. To me it can never appear like an amusing fable, or lose its interest and importance. The story is one which is continually before me, and must return fresh to my mind, with painful emotions, as long as I live. With time, and Christian instruction, and the sympathy and examples of the wise and good, I hope to learn submissively to bear whatever trials are appointed me, and to improve under them all.

Impressed as I continually am with the frightful reality of the painful communications that I have made in this volume, I can only offer to all persons who may doubt or dis-believe my statements, these two things:

Permit me to go through the Hotel Dieu Nunnery at Montreal, with some impartial ladies and gentlemen, that they may compare my account with the interior parts of the building, into which no persons but the Roman Bishop and Priests are ever admitted; and if they do not find my description true, then discard me as an impostor. Bring me before a court of justice – there I am willing to meet *Latargue, Dufresne, Phelan, Bonin,* and *Richards,* and their wicked companions, with the Superior, and any of the nuns, before a thousand men,

MARIA MONK
New York, 11th January, 1836

CHAPTER I

MY parents were both from Scotland, but had been resident in the Lower Canada some time before their marriage, which took place in Montreal, and in that city I have spent most of my life. I was born at St. John's, where they lived for a short time. My father was an officer under the British Government, and my mother has enjoyed a pension on that account ever since his death.

According to my earliest recollections, he was attentive to his family, and had a peculiar passage from the Bible, which often occurred to me in after life. I may very probably have been taught by him, as after his death I did not recollect to have received any instruction at home, and was not even brought up to read the Scriptures; my mother, although nominally a Protestant, not being accustomed to pay attention to her children. She was rather inclined to think well of the Catholics, and often attended their churches. To my want of religious instruction at home, and the ignorance of my Creator and my duty, which was its natural effect, I think I can trace my introduction to convents, and the scenes which I am to describe in the following narrative.

When about six or seven years of age, I went to school to a Mr. Workman, a Protestant, who taught in Sacrament Street, and remained several months. There I learned to read and write, and arithmetic as far as division. All the progress I ever made in those branches was gained in that school, as I have never improved in any of them since.

A number of girls of my acquaintance went to school to the nuns of the Congregational Nunnery, or Sisters of Charity, as they are sometimes called. The schools taught by them are perhaps more numerous than some of my readers may imagine. Nuns are sent out from that convent to many of the towns and villages of Canada to teach small schools; and some of them are established as instructresses in different parts of the United States. When I was about ten years old, my mother asked me one day if I should like to learn to read and write French, and then I began to think seriously of attending the school in the Congregational Nunnery. I had already some acquaintance with that language, sufficient to speak it a little, as I heard it every day, and my mother knew something of it.

I have a distinct recollection of my first entrance into the Nunnery; and the day was an important one in my life, as on it commenced my acquaintance with a convent. I was conducted by some of my young friends along Notre Dame street, till we reached the gate. Entering that, we walked some distance along the side of a building towards a chapel, until we reached a door, stopped, and rang a bell. This was soon opened, and entering, we proceeded through a long covered passage till we took a short turn to the left, soon after which we reached the door of the school-room. On my entrance, the Superior met me, and told me first of all that I must dip my fingers into the holy water at her door, cross myself, and say a short prayer; and this she told me was always required of Protestant as well as Catholic children.

There were about fifty girls in the school, and the nuns professed to teach something of reading, writing, arithmetic, and geography. The methods, however, were very imperfect, and little attention was devoted to them, the time being in a great degree engrossed with lessons in needlework, which was performed with much skill. The nuns had no very regular parts assigned them in the management of the schools. They were rather rough and unpolished in their manners, often explaining, 'C'est un mensonge' (that's a lie), and 'mon Dieu' (my God), on the most trivial occasions. Their writing was quite poor, and it was not uncommon for them to put a capital letter in the middle of a word. The only book of geography which we studied, was a catechism of geography, from which we learnt by heart a few questions and answers. We were sometimes referred to a map, but it was only to point out Montreal or Quebec, or some other prominent name, while we had no instruction beyond.

It may be necessary, for the information of some of my readers, to mention that there are three distinct Convents in Montreal, all of different kinds – that is, founded on different plans, and governed by different rules. Their names are as follows:

1. The Congregational Nunnery.
2. The Black Nunnery, or Convent of Sister Bourgeoise.
3. The Grey Nunnery.

The first of these professes to be devoted entirely to the education of girls. It would require, however, only a proper examination to prove, that with the exception of needlework, hardly anything is taught excepting prayer and catechism; the instruction in reading, writing, etc., in fact, amounting to very little, and often to nothing. This Convent is adjacent to the next to be spoken of, being separated from it only by a wall. The second professes to be a charitable institution for the care of the sick, and the supply of bread and medicines for the poor; and something is done in these departments of charity, although but an insignificant amount compared with the size of the buildings and the number of inmates.

The Grey Nunnery, which is situated in a distant part of the city, is also a large edifice, containing departments for the care of insane persons and foundlings. With this, however, I have less personal acquaintance than with either of the others. I have often seen two of the Grey nuns, and know their rules, as well as those of the Congregational Nunnery; they do not confine them always within their walls, like those of the Black Nunnery. These two Convents have their common names (Black and Grey) from the colours of the dresses worn by their inmates.

In all these three Convents there are certain apartments into which strangers can gain admittance, but others from which they are always excluded. In all, large quantities of various ornaments are made by the nuns, which are exposed for sale in the *Ornament Rooms*, and afford large pecuniary receipts every year, which contribute much to their income. In these rooms, visitors often purchase such things as please them, from some of the old and confidential nuns who have the charge of them.

From all that appears to the public eye, the nuns of these Convents are devoted to the charitable object appropriate to each, the labour of making different articles known to be manufactured by them, and the religious observances, which occupy a large portion of their time. They are regarded with much respect by the people at large; and now and then when a novice takes the veil, she is supposed to retire from the temptations and troubles of this world into a state of holy seclusion, where, by prayer, self-mortification, and good deeds, she prepares herself for heaven. Sometimes the Superior of a Convent obtains the character of working miracles: and when such an one dies, it is published through the country, and crowds throng the Convent, who think indulgences are to be derived from bits of her clothes and other things she has possessed; and many have sent articles to be touched to her bed or chair, in which a degree of virtue is thought to remain. I used to participate in such ideas and feelings, and began by degrees to look upon a nun as the happiest of women, and a Convent as the most peaceful, holy, and delightful place of abode. It is true, some pains were taken to impress such views upon me. Some of the priests of the Seminary often visited the Congregational Nunnery, and both catechized and talked with us on religion. The Superior of the Black Nunnery adjoining, also, occasionally came into the school, and enlarged on the advantage we enjoyed in having such teachers, and dropped something now and then relating to her own convent, calculated to make us entertain the highest ideas of it, and make us sometimes think of the possibility of getting into it.

Among the instructions given to us by the priests, some

of the most pointed were directed against the Protestant Bible. They often enlarged upon the evil tendency of that book, and told us that but for it many a soul condemned to hell, and suffering eternal punishment, might have been in happiness. They could not say anything in its favour; for that would be speaking against religion and against God. They warned us against its woe, and represented it as a thing very dangerous to our souls. In confirmation of this, they would repeat some of the answers taught us at catechism, a few of which I will here give. We had little catechisms, ('Les Petits Catéchismes') put into our hands to study; but the priests soon began to teach us a new set of answers, which were not to be found in our books, from some of which I have received new ideas, and got, as I thought, important light on religious subjects, which confirmed me more in my belief in the Roman Catholic doctrines. Those questions and answers I can still recall with tolerable accuracy, and some of them I will add here. I never have read them, as we were taught them only by word of mouth.

'*Question*. Pourquoi le bon Dieu n'a pas fait tous les commandements?' '*Response*. Parce que l' homme n'est pas si fort qu'il peut garder tous ses commandments.'

'*Question*. Why did not God make all the commandments?' – '*Answer*. Because man is not strong enough to keep them.'

And another: '*Q*. Pourquoi l' homme ne lit pas l' Evangile?' – '*A*. Parce que l' esprit de l' homme est trop borné et trop faible pour comprendre qu'est ce que Dieu a écrit.'

'*Q*. Why are men not to read the New Testament?' – '*A*. Because the mind of man is too limited and weak to understand what God has written.'

These questions and answers are not to be found in the common catechisms in use in Montreal and other places where I have been, but all the children in the Congregational Nunnery were taught them, and many more not found in these books.

CHAPTER II

THERE was a girl thirteen years old whom I knew in the school, who resided in the neighbourhood of my mother, and with whom I had been familiar. She told me one day at school, of the conduct of a priest with her at confession, at which I was astonished. It was of so criminal and shameful a nature, I could hardly believe it, and yet I had so much confidence that she spoke the truth, that I could not discredit it.

She was partly persuaded by the priest to believe that he could not sin, because he was a priest, and that anything he did to her would sanctify her; and yet she seemed somewhat doubtful how she should act. A priest, she had been told by him, is a holy man, and appointed to a holy office, and therefore what would be wicked in other men, could not be so in him. She told me she had informed her mother of it, who expressed no anger nor disapprobation; but only enjoined it upon her not to speak of it; and remarked to her, as priests were not like men, but holy, and sent to instruct and save us, whatever they did was right.

I afterwards confessed to the priest that I had heard the story, and had a penance to perform for indulging a sinful curiosity in making inquiries; and the girl had another for communicating it. I afterwards learnt that other children had been treated in the same manner, and also of similar proceedings.

Indeed it was not long before such language was used to me, and I well remember how my views of right and wrong were shaken by it. Another girl at the school, from a place above Montreal, called the Lac, told me the following story of what had occurred recently in that vicinity. A young squaw, called La Belle Marie (pretty Mary), had been seen going to confession at the house of the priest, who lived a little out of the village. La Belle Marie was afterwards missed, and her murdered body was found in the river. A knife was also found bearing the priest's name. Great indignation was excited among the Indians, and the priest immediately absconded, and was never heard from. A note was found on his table addressed to him, telling him to fly, if he was guilty.

It was supposed that the priest was fearful that his conduct might be betrayed by this young female; and he undertook to clear himself by killing her.

These stories struck me with surprise at first, but I gradually began to feel differently, even supposing them true, and to look upon the priests as men incapable of sin; besides, when I first went to confess, which I did to Father Richards in the old French church, since taken down, I heard nothing improper; and it was not until I had been several times that the priests became more and more bold, and were at length indecent in their questions, and even in their conduct when I confessed to them in the Sacristy. This subject, I believe, is not understood nor suspected among Protestants; and it is not my intention to speak of it very particularly, because it is impossible to do so without saying things both shameful and demoralizing.

I will only say here, that when quite a child, I heard from the mouths of the priests at confession what I cannot repeat, with treatment corresponding; and several females in Canada have assured me that they have repeatedly, and indeed regularly, been required to answer the same and other like questions, many of which present to the mind deeds which the most iniquitous and corrupt heart could hardly invent.

There was a frequent change of teachers in the school of the Nunnery, and no regular system was pursued in our instruction. There were many nuns who came and went while I was there, being frequently called in and out without any perceptible reason. They supply school teachers to many of the country towns, usually two to each of the towns with which I was acquainted, besides sending Sisters of

Charity to many parts of the United States. Among those whom I saw most was Saint Patrick, an old woman for a nun, that is about forty, very ignorant and gross in her manners, with quite a beard on her face, and very cross and disagreeable. She was sometimes our teacher in sewing, and was appointed to keep order among us. We were allowed to enter only a few of the rooms in the Congregational Nunnery, although it was not considered one of the secluded Convents.

In the Black Nunnery, which is very near the Congregational, is a hospital for sick people from the city; and sometimes some of our boarders, such as were indisposed, were sent there to be cured. I was once taken ill myself and sent there, where I remained a few days.

There were beds enough for a considerable number more. A physician attended it daily, and there are a number of the veiled nuns of that Convent who spend most of their time there.

These would also sometimes read lectures and repeat prayers to us.

After I had been in the Congregational Nunnery about two years, I left it, and attended several different schools for a short time. But I soon became dissatisfied, having many and severe trials to endure at home, which my feelings will not allow me to describe; and as my Catholic acquaintances had often spoken to me in favour of their faith, I was inclined to believe it true, although, as I before said, I knew little of any religion. While out of the nunnery, I saw nothing of religion. If I had, I believe I should never have thought of becoming a nun.

CHAPTER III

AT length I determined to become a Black Nun, and called upon one of the oldest priests in the Seminary, to whom I made known my intention.

The old priest to whom I applied was Father Rocque. He is still alive. He was at that time the oldest priest in the seminary, and carried the Bon Dieu, Good God, as the sacramental wafer is called. When going to administer it in any country place, he used to ride with a man before him, who rang a bell as a signal. When the Canadians heard it, whose habitations he passed, they would come and prostrate themselves to the earth, worshipping it as a God. He was a man of great age, and wore large curls, so that he somewhat resembled his predecessor, Father Roue. He was at that time at the head of the Seminary. This Institution is a large edifice, situated near the Congregational and Black Nunneries, being on the east side of Notre Dame Street. It is the general rendezvous and centre of all the priests in the district of Montreal, and I have been told, supplied all the country as far down as the Three Rivers, which place, I believe, is under the charge of the Seminary of Quebec. About one hundred and fifty priests are connected with that at Montreal, as every small place has one priest, and a number of larger ones have two.

Father Rocque promised to converse with the Superior of the Convent, and proposed my calling again at the end of two weeks, at which time I visited the Seminary again, and was introduced by him to the Superior of the Black Nunnery. She told me she must make some inquiries, before she could give me a decided answer, and proposed to me to take up my abode a few days at the house of a French family in St. Lawrence suburb, a distant part of the city. Here I remained about a fortnight, during which time I formed some acquaintance with the family, particularly with the mistress of the house, who was a devoted Papist, and had a high respect for the Superior, with whom she stood on good terms.

At length, on Saturday morning about ten o'clock, I called, and was admitted into the Black Nunnery as a novice, much to my satisfaction, for I had a high idea of life in a Convent, secluded, as I supposed the inmates to be, from the world and all its evil influences, and assured of ever-lasting happiness in heaven. The Superior received me, and conducted me into a large room, where the novices, who are called in French, Postulantes, were assembled, and engaged in their customary occupation of sewing.

Here were about forty of them, and they were collected in groups in different parts of the room, chiefly near the windows; but in each group was found one of the veiled nuns of the convent, whose abode was in the interior apart-ments, to which no novice was to be admitted. As we entered, the Superior informed the assembly that a new novice had come, and she desired any one present who might have known me in the world to signify it.

Two Misses Feugness, and a Miss Howard from Vermont, who had been my fellow-pupils in the Congregational Nun-nery, immediately recognized me. I was then placed in one of the groups at a distance from them, and furnished by a nun, called Sainte Clotilde, with materials to make a purse, such as priests use to carry the consecrated wafer in. when they go to administer the sacrament to the sick. I well remember my feelings at that time, sitting among a number of strangers, and expecting with painful anxiety the arrival of the dinner-hour. Then, as I knew, ceremonies were to be performed, though for which I was but ill prepared, as I had not yet heard the rules by which I was to be governed, and knew nothing of the forms to be repeated in the daily exer-cises, except the creed in Latin, and that imperfectly. This was during the time of recreation, as it is called. The only recreation there allowed, however, is that of the mind, and of this there is but little. We were kept at work, and permitted to speak with each other only in hearing of the old nuns who sat by us. We proceeded to dinner in couples, and ate in silence while a lecture was read.

The novices had access to only eight of the apartments of the Convent; and whatever else we wished to know, we could only conjecture. The sleeping room was in the second story, at the end of the western wing. The beds were placed in rows, without curtains or anything else to obstruct the view; and in one corner was a small room partitioned off, in which was the bed of a night-watch, that is, the old nun who was appointed to oversee us for the night. In each side of the partition were two holes, through which she could look out upon us whenever she pleased. Her bed was a little raised above the level of the others. There was a lamp hung in the middle of our chamber, which showed everything to her very distinctly; and as she had no light in her little room, we never could perceive whether she was awake or asleep. As we knew that the slightest deviation from the rules would expose us to her observation as well as to that of our companions, in whom it was a virtue to betray one another's faults, continual exposure to suffer what I disliked, and had my mind occupied in thinking of what I was to do next, and what I must avoid. Though I soon learned the rules and ceremonies we had to pass, which were many, and we had to be very particular in their observance. We were employed in different kinds of work while I was a novice. The most beautiful specimen of the nun's manufacture which I saw, was a rich carpet made of fine worsted, which had been begun before my acquaintance with the Convent, and was finished while I was there. This was sent as a present to the King of England, as an expression of gratitude for the money annually received from the government. It was about forty yards in length, and very handsome. We were ignorant of the amount of money thus received. The Convent of the Grey Nuns had also received funds from the government, though on some account or other, had not for several years.

I was sitting by a window at one time with a girl named Jane M'Coy, when one of the old nuns came up and spoke to us in a tone of liveliness and kindness, which seemed strange in a place where everything appeared so cold and reserved. Some remarks which she made were evidently intended to cheer and encourage me, and make me think that she felt some interest in me. I do not recollect what she said, but I remember it gave me pleasure. I also remember that her manners struck me singularly. She was rather old for a nun – that is, probably thirty; her figure large, her face wrinkled, and her dress careless. She seemed also to be under less restraint than the others, and this I afterwards found was the case. She sometimes even set the rules at defiance. She would speak aloud when silence was required, and sometimes walk about when she ought to have kept her place: she would even say and do things on purpose to make us laugh, and, although often blamed for her conduct, had her offences frequently passed over, when others would have been punished with penances.

I learnt that this woman had always been singular. She never would consent to take a saint's name on receiving the veil, and had always been known by her own, which was Jane Ray. Her irregularities were found to be numerous, and penances were of so little use in governing her, that she was pitied by some, who thought her partially insane. She was, therefore, commonly spoken of as mad Jane Ray; and when she committed a fault, it was apologized for by the Superior or other nuns, on the ground that she did not know what she did.

The occupations of a novice in the Black Nunnery are not such as some of our readers may suppose. They are not employed in studying the higher branches of education: they are not offered any advantages for storing their minds, or polishing their manners; they are not taught even reading, writing, or arithmetic; much less any of the more advanced branches of knowledge. My time was chiefly employed, at first, in work and prayers. It is true, during the last year I studied a great deal, and was required to work but very little; but it was the study of prayers in French and Latin, which I had merely to commit to memory, to prepare for the easy repetition of them on my reception, and after I should be admitted as a nun.

Among the wonderful events which had happened in the Convent, that of the sudden conversion of a gay young lady of the city into a nun appeared to me one of the most remarkable. The story which I first heard while a novice, made a deep impression upon my mind. It was nearly as follows:

The daughter of a wealthy citizen of Montreal was passing the church of Bon Secours one evening, on her way to a ball, when she was suddenly thrown down upon the steps or near the door, and received a severe shock. She was taken up, and removed first, I think, into the church, but soon into the Black Nunnery, which she determined to join as a nun; instead, however, of being required to pass through a long novitiate (which usually occupies about two years and a half, and is abridged only where the character is peculiarly exemplary and devout), she was permitted to take the veil without delay, being declared by God to a priest to be in a state of sanctity. The meaning of this expression is, that she was a real saint, and already in a great measure raised above the world and its influences, and incapable of sinning; possessing the power of intercession, and a proper object to be addressed in prayer. This remarkable individual, I was further informed, was still in the Convent, though I never was allowed to see her; she did not mingle with the other nuns, either at work, or worship, or meals; for she had no need of food, and not only her soul, but her body, was in heaven a great part of her time. What added, if possible, to the reverence and mysterious awe with which I thought of her, was the fact I learned, that she had no name. The titles used in speaking of her were: the holy saint, reverend mother, or saint bon pasteur (the holy good shepherd).

It is wonderful that we could have carried our reverence for the Superior so far as we did, although it was the direct tendency of many instructions and regulations, indeed of the whole system, to permit, even to foster, a superstitious regard for her. One of us was occasionally called into her room to cut her nails, or dress her hair; and we would often collect the clippings, and distribute them to each other, or preserve them with the utmost care. I once picked up all her stray hairs I could find after combing her head, bound them together, and kept them for some time, until she told me I was not worthy to possess things so sacred. Jane M'Coy and I were once sent to alter a dress for the Superior. I gathered up all the bits of thread, made a little bag, and put them into it for safe preservation. This I wore a long time round my neck, so long, indeed, that I wore out a number of strings, which I remember I had replaced with new ones. I believed it to possess the power of removing pain, and have often prayed to it to cure the toothache, &c. Jane Ray sometimes professed to outdo us all in devotion to the Superior, and would pick up the feathers after making her bed. These she would distribute among us, saying, 'When the Superior dies, relics will begin to grow scarce, and you had better supply yourselves in season.' Then she would treat the whole matter in some way to turn it into ridicule. Equally contradictory would she appear, when occasionally she would obtain leave from her Superior to tell her dreams. With a serious face, which sometimes imposed upon all of us, and made us half believe she was in a perfect state of sanctity, she would narrate in French some unaccountable vision which she said she had enjoyed; then turning round, would say, 'There are some who do not understand me; you all ought to be informed.' And then she would say something totally different in English, which put us to the greatest agony for fear of laughing. Sometimes she would say she expected to be Superior herself one of those days, and other things which I have not room to repeat.

While I was in the Congregational Nunnery, I had gone to the parish church whenever I was to confess, for although the nuns had a private confession-room in the building, the boarders were taken in parties through the streets, on different days, by some of the nuns, to confess in the church; but in the Black Nunnery, as we had a chapel, and priests attending in the confessionals, we never left the building.

Our confessions there as novices were always performed in one way, so that it may be sufficient to describe a single case. Those of us who were to confess at a particular time, took our places on our knees near the confession-box, and, after having repeated a number of prayers, &c., prescribed in our book, came up one at a time and kneeled beside a fine wooden lattice-work, which entirely separated the confessor from us, yet permitted us to place our faces almost to his ear, and nearly concealed his countenance from our view, even when so near. I recollect how the priests used to recline their heads on one side, and often covered their faces with their handkerchiefs, while they heard me confess my sins, and put questions to me, which were often of the most improper and revolting nature, naming crimes both unthought of and inhuman. Still, strange as it may seem, I was persuaded to believe that all this was their duty, or at least that it was done without sin.

Veiled nuns would often appear in the chapel at confession; though, as I understood, they generally confessed in private. Of the plan of their confession-rooms I had no information; but I supposed the ceremony to be conducted much on the same plan as in the chapel and in the church, viz., with a lattice interposed between the confessor and the confessing.

Punishments were sometimes resorted to while I was a novice, though but seldom. The first time I ever saw a gag, was one day when a young novice had done something to offend the Superior. This girl I always had compassion for, because she was very young, and an orphan. The Superior sent for a gag, and expressed her regret at being compelled, by the bad conduct of the child, to proceed to such a punishment; after which she put it into her mouth, so far as to keep it open, and then let it remain for some time before she took it out. There was a leathern strap fastened to each end, and buckled to the back part of the head.

CHAPTER IV

AFTER I had been a novice four or five years, that is, from the time I commenced school in the Convent, one day I was treated by one of the nuns in a manner which displeased me, and because I expressed some resentment, I was required to beg her pardon. Not being satisfied with this, although I complied with the command, nor with the coldness with which the Superior treated me, I determined to quit the Convent at once, which I did without asking leave. There would have been no obstacle to my departure, I presume, novice as I then was, if I had asked permission; but I was too much displeased to wait for that, and went home without speaking to anyone on the subject.

I soon after visited the town of St. Denis, where I saw two young ladies with whom I had formerly been acquainted in Montreal, and one of them a former school-mate at Mr. Workman's school. After some conversation with me, and learning that I had known a lady who kept a school in the place, they advised me to apply to her to be employed as her assistant teacher; for she was then instructing the government school in that place.

I visited her, and found her willing, and I was engaged at once as her assistant.

The government society paid her £20 a year; she was obliged to teach ten children gratuitously; she might have fifteen pence a month, about a quarter of a dollar, for each ten scholars more, and then she was at liberty, according to the regulations, to demand as much as she pleased for the other pupils. The course of instruction as required by the society, embraced only reading, writing, and what was called ciphering, though I think improperly. The only books used were a spelling-book, l'Instruction de la Jeunesse, the Catholic New Testament, and l'Histoire du Canada. When these had been read through, in regular succession, the children were dismissed as having completed their education. No difficulty is found in making the common French Canadians content with such an amount of instruction as this; on the contrary, it is often found very hard indeed to prevail upon them to send their children at all, for they say it takes too much of the love of God from them to send them to school. The teacher strictly complied with the requisitions of the society in whose employment she was, and the Roman Catholic catechism was regularly taught in the school, as much from choice, as from submission to the authority, as she was a strict Catholic. I had brought with me the little bag before mentioned, in which I had so long kept the clippings of the thread left after making a dress for the Superior. Such was my regard for it, that I continued to wear it constantly round my neck, and to feel the same reverence for its supposed virtues as before. I occasionally had the toothache during my stay at St. Denis, and then always relied on the influence of my little bag. On such occasions I would say –'By virtue of this bag may I be delivered from the toothache!' and I supposed that when it ceased it was owing to that cause.

While engaged in this manner, I became acquainted with a man who soon proposed marriage; and, young and ignorant of the world as I was, I heard his offers with favour. On consulting with my friend, she expressed a friendly interest in me, advised me against taking such a step, and especially as I knew so little about the man, except that a report was circulated unfavourable to his character. Unfortunately, I was not wise enough to listen to her advice, and hastily married. In a few weeks I had occasion to repent of the step I had taken, as the report proved true – a report which I thought justified, and indeed required, our separation. After I had been in St. Denis about three months, finding myself thus situated, and not knowing what else to do, I determined to return to the Convent, and pursue my former intention of becoming a Black Nun, could I gain admittance. Knowing the many inquiries the Superior would make relative to me during my absence, before leaving St. Denis I agreed with the lady with whom I had been associated as a teacher (when she went to Montreal, which she did very frequently) to say to the Lady Superior I had been under her protection during my absence, which would satisfy and stop further inquiry, as I was sensible, should they know, I had been married, I should not gain admittance.

I soon left and returned to Montreal, and, on reaching the city, I visited the Seminary, and in another inverview with the Superior of it, communicated my wish, and desired her to procure my re-admission as a novice. Little delay occurred.

After leaving for a short time, she returned and told me that the Superior of the Convent had consented, and I was soon introduced into her presence.

She blamed me for my conduct in leaving the nunnery, but told me that I ought to be ever grateful to my guardian angel for taking care of me, unless prohibited by the Superior; and this she promised me. The money usually required for the admission of novices had not been expected from me. I had been admitted the first time without any such requisition; but now I chose to pay for my re-admission. I knew that she was able to dispense with such a demand as well in this as in the former case, and she knew that I was not in possession of anything like the sum required.

But I was bent on paying to the Nunnery, and accustomed to receive the doctrine often repeated to me before that time, that when the advantage of the church was consulted, the steps taken were justifiable, let them be what they would; I therefore resolved to obtain money on false pretences, confident that if all were known, I should be far from displeasing the Superior. I went to the brigade-major, and asked him to give me the money payable to my mother from her pension, which amounted to about thirty dollars, and without questioning my authority to receive it in her name, he gave it to me.

From several of their friends I obtained small sums under the name of loans, so that altogether I had soon raised a number of pounds, with which I hastened to the Nunnery, and deposited a part in the hands of the Superior. She received the money with evident satisfaction, though she must have known that I could not have obtained it honestly; and I was at once re-admitted as a novice.

Much to my gratification, not a word fell from the lips of any of my old associates in relation to my unceremonious departure, nor my voluntary return. The Superior's orders, I had not a doubt, had been explicitly laid down, and they certainly were carefully obeyed, for I never heard an allusion made to that subject during my subsequent stay in the Convent, except that, when alone, the Superior would sometimes say a little about it.

There were numbers of young ladies who entered awhile as novices, and became weary or disgusted with some things they observed, and remained but a short time. One of my cousins, who lived at Lachine, named Reed, spent about a fortnight in the Convent with me. She, however, conceived such an antipathy to the priests, that she used expressions which offended the Superior.

The first day that she attended mass, while at dinner with us in full community, she said before us all, 'What a rascal that priest was, to preach against his best friend!'

All stared at such an unusual exclamation, and someone inquired what she meant.

'I say,' she continued, 'he has been preaching against him who has given him his bread. Do you suppose that if there were no devil, there would be any priests?'

This bold young novice was immediately dismissed, and in the afternoon we had a long sermon from the Superior on the subject.

It happened that I one day got a leaf of an English Bible which had been brought into the Convent, wrapped around some sewing silk, purchased at a store in the city. For some reason or other, I determined to commit to memory a chapter it contained, which I soon did. It is the only chapter I ever learnt in the Bible, and I can now repeat it. It is the second of St. Matthew's gospel. 'Now when Jesus was born at Bethlehem in Judea,' &c. It happened that I was observed reading the paper, and when the nature of it was discovered I was condemned to do penance for my offence.

Great dislike to the Bible was shown by those who conversed with me about it, and several have remarked to me at different times, that if it were not for that book, Catholics would never be led to renounce their own faith.

I have heard passages read from the Evangile, relating to the death of Christ; the conversion of Paul; a few chapters from St. Matthew, and perhaps a few others. The priests would also sometimes take a verse or two, and preach from it. I have read St. Peter's life, but only in the book called the 'Lives of the Saints.' He, I understood, has the keys of heaven and hell, and has founded our church. As for Saint Paul, I remember, as I was taught to understand it, that he was once a great persecutor of the Roman Catholics until he became convicted, and confessed to one of the father confessors, I don't know which. For who can expect to be forgiven, who does not become a Catholic, and confess?

CHAPTER V

THE day on which I received Confirmation was a distressing one to me. I believed the doctrine of the Roman Catholics, and according to them I was guilty of three mortal sins: concealing something at confession; sacrilege, in putting the body of Christ in the sacrament at my feet, and by receiving it while not in a state of grace! and now I had been led into all those sins in consequence of my marriage, which I never had acknowledged, as it would have cut me off from being admitted as a nun.

On the day, therefore, when I went to the church to be confirmed with a number of others, I suffered extremely from the reproaches of my conscience. I knew, at least I believed, as I had been told, that a person who had been anointed with the holy oil of confirmation on the forehead, and dying in the state in which I was, would go down to hell, and, in the place where the oil had been rubbed, the names of my sins would blaze out of my forehead; these would be a sign by which the devils would know me, and would torment me the worse for them. I was thinking of all this while I was sitting in the pew, waiting to receive the oil. I felt, however, some consolation, as I often did afterwards, when my sins came to my mind: and this consolation I derived from another doctrine of the church, viz., that a bishop could absolve me from all these sins any minute before my death; and I intended to confess them all to a bishop before leaving the world. At length the moment for administering of the 'sacrament arrived, and a bell was rung. Those who had come to be confirmed had brought tickets from their confessors, and those were thrown into a hat, and carried around by a priest, who in turn handed each to a bishop, by which he learned the name of each of us, and applied a little of the oil to the foreheads. This was immediately rubbed off by a priest with a bit of cloth quite roughly.

I went home with some qualms of conscience, and often thought with dread of the following tale, which I have heard told, to illustrate the sinfulness of conduct like mine.

A priest was once travelling, when just as he was passing by a house, his horse fell on his knees, and would not rise. His rider dismounted and went in, to learn the cause of so extraordinary an occurrence. He found there a woman near death, to whom a priest was trying to administer the

sacrament, but without success; for every time she attempted to swallow it, it was thrown back out of her mouth into
the chalice. He perceived it was owing to unconfessed sin,
and took away the holy wafer from her: on which his horse
rose from his knees, and he pursued his journey.

I often remembered also that I had been told, that we
shall have as many devils biting us, if we go to hell, as we
have unconfessed sins on our consciences.

I was required to devote myself for about a year to the
study of the prayers and practice of the ceremonies necessary on the reception of a nun. This I found a very tedious
duty: but as I was released in a great degree from the daily
labours usually demanded of novices, I felt little disposition
to complain.

CHAPTER VI

I was introduced into the Superior's room on the evening
preceding the day on which I was to take the veil, to have
an interview with the bishop. The Superior was present,
and the interview lasted about half an hour. The bishop on
this, as on other occasions, appeared to be habitually rough
in his manners. His address was by no means prepossessing.

Before I took the veil, I was ornamented for the ceremony,
and was clothed in a dress belonging to the Convent, which
was used on such occasions; and placed not far from the
altar in the chapel, in the view of a number of spectators,
who had assembled, in number, perhaps about forty.
Taking the veil is an affair which occurs so frequently in
Montreal, that it has long ceased to be regarded as a
novelty; and, although notice had been given in the French
parish church as usual, only a small audience assembled
as I have mentioned.

Being well prepared with a long training, and frequent
rehearsals, for what I was to perform, I stood waiting in my

large flowing dress for the appearance of the bishop. He soon presented himself, entering by a door behind the altar; I then threw myself at his feet, and asked him to confer upon me the veil. He expressed his consent; and then turning to the Superior, I threw myself prostrate at her feet, according to my instructions, repeating what I had before done at rehearsals, and made a movement as if to kiss her feet. This she prevented, or appeared to prevent, catching me by a sudden motion of her hand, and granted my request. I then kneeled before the Holy Sacrament, that is a large round wafer held by the Bishop between his fore-finger and thumb, and made my vows.

This wafer I had been taught to regard with the utmost veneration as the real body of Jesus Christ, the presence of which made the vows that were uttered before it binding in the most solemn manner.

After taking the vows I proceeded to a small apartment behind the altar, accompanied by four nuns, where there was a coffin prepared with my nun's name engraved upon it:

'SAINT EUSTACE.'

My companions lifted it by four handles attached to it, while I threw off my dress, and put on that of a nun of Sœur Bourgeoise; and then we all returned to the chapel. I proceeded first, and was followed by four nuns, the Bishop naming a number of worldly pleasures in rapid succession, in reply to which I as rapidly repeated, 'Je renonce, je renonce, je renonce, – I renounce, I renounce, I renounce.

The coffin was then placed in front of the altar, and I advanced to place myself in it. This coffin was to be deposited, after the ceremony in an out-house, to be preserved until my death, when it was to receive my corpse. There were reflections which I naturally made at that time, but I stepped in, extended myself, and lay still. A pillow had been placed at the head of the coffin, to support my head in a comfortable position. A large thick black cloth was then spread over me, and the chanting of Latin hymns immediately commenced. My thoughts were not the most pleasing during the time I lay in that direction. The pall, or Drap Mortel, as the cloth is called, had a strong smell of incense, which was always disagreeable to me, and then proved almost suffocating. I recollected the story of the novice, who, in taking the veil, lay down in her coffin like me, and was covered in the same manner, but on the removal of the covering was found dead.

When I was uncovered, I rose, stepped out of my coffin, and kneeled. Other ceremonies then followed, of no particular interest; after which the music commenced, and here the whole was finished. I then proceeded from the chapel, and returned to the Superior's room, followed by the other nuns, who walked two by two, in their customary manner with their hands folded on their breasts, and their eyes cast down upon the floor. The nun who was to be my companion in future, then walked at the end of the procession. On reaching the Superior's door they all left me, and I entered alone, and found her with the Bishop and two Priests.

The Superior now informed me that having taken the black veil, it only remained that I should swear the three oaths customary on becoming a nun; and that some explanation would be necessary from her. I was now, she told me, to have access to every part of the edifice, even to the cellar, where two of the sisters were imprisoned for causes which she did not mention. I must be informed that one of my great duties was to obey the priests in all things; and this I soon learnt, to my utter astonishment and horror, was to live in the practice of criminal intercourse with them. I expressed some of the feelings which this announcement excited in me, which came upon me like a flash of lightning; but the only effect was to set her arguing with me, in favour of the crime, representing it as a virtue acceptable to God, and honourable to me. The priests, she said, were not situated like other men, being forbidden to marry; while they lived secluded, laborious, and self-denying lives for our salvation. They might, indeed, be considered our saviours, as without their service we could not obtain pardon of sin, and must go to hell. Now it was our solemn duty, on withdrawing from the world, to consecrate our lives to religion, to practise every species of self-denial. We could not be too humble, nor mortify our feelings too far; this was to be done by opposing them, and acting contrary to them; and what she proposed was, therefore, pleasing in the sight of God. I now felt how foolish I had been to place myself in the power of such persons as were around me.

From what she said, I could draw no other conclusions but that I was required to act like the most abandoned of beings, and that all my future associations were habitually guilty of the most heinous and detestable crimes. When I repeated my expressions of surprise and horror, she told me that such feelings were very common at first, and that many other nuns had expressed themselves as I did, who had long since changed their minds. She even said, that on her entrance into the nunnery, she had felt like me.

Doubts, she declared, were among our greatest enemies. They would lead us to question every point of duty, and induce us to waver at every step. They arose only from remaining imperfections, and were always evidences of sin. Our only way was to dismiss them immediately, repent and confess them. Priests, she insisted, could not sin. It was a thing impossible. Everything that they did, and wished, was of course right. She hoped I would see the reasonableness and duty of the oaths I was then to take, and be faithful to them.

She gave me another piece of information, which excited other feelings in me, scarcely less dreadful. Infants were sometimes born in the Convent, but they were always baptized, and immediately strangled. This secured their everlasting happiness; for the baptism purifies them from all sinfulness, and being sent out of the world before they had time to do anything wrong, they were at once admitted into heaven. How happy, she exclaimed, are those who secure immortal happiness to such little beings! Their souls would thank those who kill their bodies, if they had it in their power.

Into what a place, and among what society, had I been admitted! How different did a convent now appear from what I supposed it to be. The holy women I had always fancied the nuns to be, the venerable Lady Superior, what are they? And the priests of the Seminary adjoining, (some of whom, indeed, I had reason to think were base and profligate men,) what were they all? I now learned that they were often admitted into the nunnery, and allowed to indulge in the greatest crimes, which they and others call virtues.

And having listened for some time to the Superior alone, a number of the nuns were admitted, and took a free part in the conversation. They concurred in everything which she told me, and repeated, without any signs of shame or compunction, things which incriminated themselves. I must acknowledge the truth, and declare that all this had an effect upon my mind. I questioned whether I might not be in the wrong, and felt as if their reasoning might have some just foundation. I had been several years under the tuition of Catholics, and was ignorant of the Scriptures, and unaccustomed to the society, example, and conversation of Protestants; had not heard any appeal to the Bible as authority, but had been taught both by precept and example, to receive as truth everything said by the priests. I had not heard their authority questioned, nor anything said of any other standard of faith but their declarations. I had long been familiar with the corrupt and licentious expressions which some of them use at confessions, and believed that other women were also. I had no standard of duty to refer to, and no judgment of my own which I knew how to use, or thought of using.

All around me insisted that my doubts proved only my own ignorance and sinfulness; that they knew by experience that they would soon give place to true knowledge, and an advance in religion; and I felt something like indecision.

Still there was so much that disgusted me in the discovery I had now made, of the debased characters around me, that I would most gladly have escaped from the nunnery, and never returned. But that was a thing not to be thought of. I was in their power, and this I deeply felt, while I thought there was not one among the whole number of nuns to whom I could look for kindness. There was one, however, who began to speak to me at length in a tone that gained something of my confidence – the nun whom I have mentioned before as distinguished by her oddity, Jane Ray, who made us so much amusement when I was a novice. Although, as I have remarked, there was nothing in her face, form, or manners, to give me any pleasure, she addressed me with apparent friendliness; and while she seemed to concur with some things spoken by them, took an opportunity to whisper a few words in my ear, unheard by them, intimating that I had better comply with everything the Superior desired, if I would save my life. I was somewhat alarmed before, but I now became much more so, and determined to make no further resistance. The Superior then made me repeat the three oaths; and, when I had sworn them, I was shown into one of the community-rooms, and remained some time with the nuns, who were released from their usual employments, and enjoying a recreation day, on account of the admission of a new sister. My feelings during the remainder of the day I shall not attempt to describe, but pass on to mention the ceremonies that took place at dinner. This description may give an idea of the manner in which we always took our meals, although there were some points in which the breakfast and supper were different.

At eleven o'clock the bell rang for dinner, and the nuns all took their places in a double row, in the same order as that in which they left the chapel in the morning, except that my companion and myself were stationed at the head of the line. Standing thus for a moment, with our hands placed one on the other over the breast, and hidden in our large cuffs, with our heads bent forward, and eyes fixed on the floor, an old nun, who stood at the door, clapped her hands as a signal for us to proceed; and the procession moved on, while we all commenced the repetition of litanies. We walked on in this order, repeating all the way until we reached the door of the dining-room, where we were divided into two lines; those on the right passing down the side of the long table, and those on the left the other, till all were in; and each stopped in her place. The plates were all arranged, each with a knife, fork, and spoon, rolled up in a napkin, and tied round with a linen band marked with the owner's name. My own plate, knife, &c., were prepared like the rest: and on the band around them I found my new name written—'Saint Eustace.'

There we stood till all had concluded the litany, when the old nun, who had taken her place at the head of the table next the door, said the prayer before meat, beginning, 'Benedicite,' and we sat down. I do not remember of what our dinner consisted, but we usually had soup, and some plain dish of meat; the remains of which were occasionally served up at supper as a fricassée. One of the nuns, who had been appointed to read that day, rose, and began a lecture from a book put into her hands by the Superior, while the rest of us ate in perfect silence. The nun who reads during dinner, stays afterwards to dine. As fast as we finished our meals, each rolled up her knife, fork, and spoon, in her napkin, and bound them together with the band, and sat with hands folded. The old nun then said a short prayer, arose, stepped a little aside, clapped her hands, and we marched towards the door, bowed as we passed, before a little chapel, or glass box, containing a wax image of the infant Jesus.

Nothing important occurred till late in the afternoon, when, as I was sitting in the community-room, Father Dufresne called me out, saying, he wished to speak with me. I feared what was his intention; but I dared not disobey. In a private apartment, he treated me in a brutal manner; and, from two other priests, I afterwards received similar usage that evening. Father Dufresne afterwards appeared again; and I was compelled to remain in company with him until morning.

I am assured that the conduct of priests in our Convent had never been exposed, and it is not imagined by the people of the United States. This induces me to say what I do, notwithstanding the strong reasons I have to let it remain unknown. Still I cannot force myself to speak on such subjects except in the most brief manner.

CHAPTER VII

On Thursday morning, the bell rang at half-past six to waken us. The old nun who was acting as night-watch immediately spoke aloud:

'Voici le Seigneur qui vient.' (Behold the Lord cometh). The nuns all responded:

'Allons-y devant Lui.' (Let us go and meet him).

We then rose immediately, and dressed as expeditiously as possible, stepping into the passage-way, at the foot of our bed, as soon as we were ready, and taking place each beside her opposite companion. Thus we were soon drawn up in a double row the whole length of the room, with our hands folded across our breasts, and concealed in the broad cuffs of our sleeves. Not a word was uttered. When the signal was given, we all proceeded to the community-room, which is spacious, and took our places in rows facing the entrance, near which the Superior was seated in a vergiere.

We first repeated 'Au nom du Père, du Fils, et du Saint Espirit—Ainsi soit-il.' (in the name of the Father, the Son, and the Holy Ghost – Amen).

We then kneeled and kissed the floor; then, still on our knees, we said a very long prayer, beginning: 'Divin Jésus, Sauveur de mon âme' (Divine Jesus, Saviour of my soul). Then came the Lord's prayers, three Hail

Marys, four creeds, and five confessions (Je confesse à Dieu).

Next we repeated the ten commandments. Then we repeated the acts of faith, and a prayer to the Virgin, in
Latin, which like everything else in Latin, I never understood
a word of. Next we said litanies of the Holy Name of
Jesus, in Latin, which were afterwards to be repeated several
times in the course of the day. Then came the prayer for
the beginning of the day; then bending down, we commenced the Oraison Mental (or Mental Orison), which lasted
about an hour and a half.

This exercise was considered peculiarly solemn. We were
told in the nunnery that a certain saint was saved by the
use of it, as she never omitted it. It consists of several parts:
First, the Superior read to us a chapter from a book, which
occupied five minutes. Then profound silence prevailed for
fifteen minutes, during which we were meditating upon it.
Then she read another chapter of equal length on a different
subject, and we meditated upon that another quarter of an
hour; and after a third reading and meditation, we finished
the exercise with a prayer, called an act of contrition, in
which we asked forgiveness for the sins committed during
the Orison.

During this hour and a half I became very weary, having
before been kneeling for some time, and having then to sit
in another position more uncomfortable, with my feet under
me, and my hands clasped, and my body went humbly forward, with my head bowed down.

When the orison was over, we all rose to the upright kneeling posture, and repeated several prayers, and the litanies
of the providences, 'providence de Dieu,' &c., then followed
a number of Latin prayers, which we repeated on the way to
mass, for in the nunnery we had mass daily.

When mass was over we proceeded in our usual order to
the eating-room to breakfast, practising the same forms
which I have described at dinner. Having made our meal
in silence, we repeated the litanies of the 'holy name of
Jesus', as we proceeded to the community-room; and such

as had not finished them on their arrival, threw themselves
upon their knees, and remained there until they had gone
through with them, and then each one of us kissing the floor,
we all arose to our feet again.

At nine o'clock commenced the lecture, which was read
by a nun appointed to perform that duty that day; all the
rest of us in the room being engaged in work.

The nuns were at this time distributed in different community rooms, at different kinds of work, and each was
listening to a lecture. This exercise continued until ten
o'clock, when the recreation-bell rang. We still continued
our work, but the nuns began to converse with each other,
on subjects permitted by the rules, in the hearing of the old
nuns, one of whom was seated in each of the groups.

At half past ten the silence-bell rang, and this conversation instantly ceased, and the recitation of some Latin
prayers commenced, which continued half an hour.

At eleven o'clock the dinner-bell rang, and we went
through the forms and ceremonies of the preceding day.
We proceeded two by two. The old nun who had the command of us, clapped her hands as the first couple reached
the door, when we stopped. The first two dipped their fingers
into the font, touched the holy water to the breast, forehead,
and each side, thus forming a cross, said, 'In the name of
the Father, Son, and Holy Ghost, Amen,' and then walked
on to the dining-room repeating the litanies. The rest followed their example. On reaching the door the couples divided and the two rows of nuns marched up, stopped, and
faced the table against their plates. There we stood, repeating the close of the litany aloud. The old nuns pronounced

'BENEDICITE,'

and we sat down. One of our number began to read a lecture,
which continued during the whole meal; she stays to eat
after the rest have retired. When we had dined, each of us
folded up our napkin, and again folded her hands. The
old nun then repeated a short prayer in French, and

stepping aside from the head of the table, let us pass out as
we came in. Each of us bowed in passing the little chapel
near the door, which is a glass case, containing a waxen
figure of the infant Jesus. When we reached the community-
room we took our places in rows, and kneeled upon the floor,
while a nun read aloud: 'Douleurs de notre Sainte Marie',
(the sorrows of our Holy Mary). At the end of each verse we
responded 'Ave Maria.' We then repeated again the litany
of the providences and the

'BENISSANTE'.

Then we kissed the floor, and rising, took our work, with
leave to converse on permitted subjects – this is what is called
recreation – till one o'clock. We then began to repeat litanies, one at a time in succession, still engaged in sewing,
for an hour.

At two o'clock commenced the afternoon lectures, which
lasted till near three. At that hour one of the nuns stood
up in the middle of the room, and asked each of us a question out of the catechism; and such as were unable to answer
correctly were obliged to kneel, until that exercise was concluded, upon as many dry peas as there were verses in the
chapter out of which they were questioned. This seems like
a penance of no great importance; but I have sometimes
kneeled on peas until I suffered great inconvenience, and
even pain. It soon makes one feel as if needles were running through the skin; whoever thinks it a trifle had better
try it.

At four o'clock recreation commenced, when we were
allowed, as usual, to speak to each other while at work.

At half past four we began to repeat prayers in Latin,
while we worked, and concluded about five o'clock, when
we commenced repeating the 'prayers for the examination
of conscience', the 'prayer after confession', the 'prayer
before sacrament', and the 'prayer after sacrament'. Thus
we continued our work until dark, when we laid it aside,
and began to go over the same prayers which we had re-

peated in the morning, with the exception of the orison mental; instead of that long exercise, we examined our consciences, to determine whether we had performed the resolution we had made in the morning, and such as had kept it repeated an 'acte de joie', or expression of gratitude; while such as had not, said an 'acte de contrition'.

When the prayers were concluded, any nun who had been disobedient in the day, knelt and asked pardon of the Superior and her companions 'for the scandal she had caused them', and then requested the Superior to give her a penance to perform. When all the penances had been imposed, we all proceeded to the eating-room to supper, repeating litanies on the way.

At supper, the ceremonies were the same as at dinner, except that there was no lecture read. We ate in silence, and went out bowing to the chapel, and repeating litanies. Returning to the community-room, which we had left, we had more prayers to repeat, which are called La couronne (crown), which consists of the following parts:

ıst. Four Paternosters.
2nd. Four Ave Marias.
3rd. Four Gloria Patrias.
4th. Bénissez, Santeys.

At the close of these we kissed the floor; after which we had recreation till half past eight o'clock, being allowed to converse on permitted subjects, but closely watched, and not allowed to sit in the corners.

At half past eight a bell was rung, and a chapter was read to us, in a book of meditations, to employ our minds upon during our waking hours at night.

Standing near the door, we dipped our fingers in the holy water, crossed and blessed ourselves, and proceeded up to the sleeping-room in the usual order, two by two.

When we had got into bed, we repeated a prayer beginning with—

'Mon Dieu, je vous donne mon coeur,'—
'My God, I give you my heart,'

and then an old nun, bringing some holy water, sprinkled
it on our beds to drive away the devil, while we took some
and crossed ourselves again.

At nine o'clock the bell rang, and all who were awake
repeated a prayer, called the offrande; those who were
asleep were considered as excused.

After my admission among the nuns, I had more opportunity than before to observe the conduct of mad Jane Ray.
She behaved quite differently from the rest, and with a degree of levity irreconcilable with the rules. She was, as I
have described her, a large woman, with nothing beautiful
or attractive in her face, form, or manners; careless in her
dress, and of a restless disposition, which prevented her from
applying herself to anything for any length of time, and
kept her roving about, and almost perpetually talking to
somebody or other. It would be very difficult to give an
accurate description of this singular woman; dressed in the
plain garments of the nuns, bound by the same vows, and
accustomed to the same life, resembling them in nothing
else, and frequently interrupting all their employments.
She was apparently almost always studying, or pursuing
some odd fancy; now rising from sewing to walk up and
down, or straying in from another apartment, looking about,
addressing some of us, and passing out again, or saying
something to make us laugh. But what showed she was no
novelty, was the little attention paid to her, and the levity
with which she was treated by all the nuns; even the
Superior every day passed over irregularities in this singular
person, which she would have punished with penances, or
at least have met with reprimands, in any other. From what
I saw of her I soon perceived that she betrayed two distinct
traits of character; a kind disposition towards such as she
chose to prefer, and a pleasure in teasing those she disliked,
or such as had offended her.

CHAPTER VIII

I WILL now give from memory a general description of the
interior of the Convent of Black Nuns, except the few apartments which I never saw. I may be inaccurate in some
things, as the apartments and passages of that spacious
building are numerous and various; but I am willing to risk
my credit for truth and sincerity on the general correspondence between my description and things as they are. And
this would, perhaps, be as good a case as any by which to test
the truth of my statements, were it possible to obtain access
to the interior. It is well known, that none but veiled nuns,
the bishop and priests, are ever admitted, and, of course,
that I cannot have seen what I profess to describe, if I have
not been a black nun. The priests who read this book will
acknowledge to themselves the truth of my description;
but will, of course, deny it to the world, and probably exert
themselves to destroy my credit. I offer to every reader the
following description, knowing that time may possibly
throw open those sacred recesses, and allow the entrance of
those who can satisfy themselves, with their own eyes, of its
truth. Some of my declarations may be thought deficient in
evidence, and this they must of necessity be in the present
state of things. But here is a kind of evidence, on which I
rely, as I see how unquestionable and satisfactory it must
prove, whenever it shall be obtained.

If the interior of the Black Nunnery, whenever it shall be
examined, is materially different from the following description, then I shall claim no confidence of my readers. If
it resembles it, they will, I presume, place confidence in
some of these declarations, on which I may never be corrob-
orated by true and living witnesses.

I am sensible that great changes may be made in the furniture of apartments; that new walls may be constructed, or
old ones removed; and I have been incredibly informed,

that masons have been employed in the Nunnery since I
left it. I well know, however, that entire changes cannot be
made, and that enough must remain as it was to substantiate
my description, whenever the truth shall be known.

The First Storey

Beginning at the extremity of the western wing of the Convent towards Notre Dame Street, on the first storey, there
is—

1st. The Nuns' private chapel adjoining which is a passage to a small projection of the building extending from
the upper storey to the ground, with very small windows.
Into the passages we were sometimes required to bring wood
from the yard, and pile it up for use.

2nd. A large community-room, with plain benches fixed
against the wall to sit, and lower ones in front to place our
feet upon. There is a fountain in the passage near the
chimney at the further end, for washing the hands and
face, with a green curtain sliding on a rod before it. This
passage leads to the old nuns' sleeping-room on the right,
and the Superior's sleeping-room just beyond it, as well as
to a stair-case which conducts to the nuns' sleeping-room,
or dormitoire above. At the end of the passage is a door
opening into—

3rd. The dining-room: this is larger than the community-room, and has three long tables for eating, and a
chapelle, or collection of little pictures, a crucifix, and a small
image of the infant Saviour in a glass case. This apartment
has four doors, by the first of which we are supposed to have
entered, while one opens to a pantry, and the third and
fourth to the two next apartments.

4th. A large community-room, with tables for sewing,
and a stair-case on the opposite left-hand corner.

5th. A community-room for prayer used by both nuns
and novices. In the further right-hand corner is a small
room, partitioned off, called the room for examination of

conscience, which I had visited while a novice by permission of the Superior, and where nuns and novices occasionally resorted to reflect on their character, usually in preparation for the sacrament, or when they had transgressed some of their rules. This little room was hardly large enough to contain half a dozen persons at a time.

6th. Next, beyond, is a large community-room for Sundays. A door leads to the yard, and thence to a gate in the wall on the cross street.

7th. Adjoining this is a sitting-room, fronting on the cross street, with two windows, and a store room on the side opposite them. There is but little furniture, and that very plain.

8th. From this room a door leads into what I may call the wax-room, as it contains many figures in wax, not intended for sale. There we sometimes used to pray, or meditate on the Saviour's Passion. This room projects from the main building; leaving it, you enter a long passage, with cupboards on the right, in which are stored crockeryware, knives and forks, and other articles of table furniture, to replace those worn out or broken – all of the plainest description; also, shovels, tongs, &c. This passage leads to—

9th. A corner room, with a few benches, &c., and a door leading to a gate in the street. Here some of the medicines were kept, and persons were often admitted on business, or to obtain medicines with tickets from the priests; and waited till the Superior or an old nun could be sent for. Beyond this room we never were allowed to go; and I cannot speak from personal knowledge of what came next.

The Second Storey

Beginning, as before, at the western extremity of the north wing, but on the second storey, the furthest apartment in that direction which I ever entered was—

1st. The nun's sleeping-room, or dormitoire, which I have already described. Here is an access to the projection mentioned in speaking of the first storey. The stairs by which we came up to bed are at the further end of the room; and near them a crucifix and font of holy water. A door at the end of the room opens into a passage, with two small rooms, and closets between them, containing bed-clothes. Next you enter—

2nd. A small community-room, beyond which is a passage with a narrow staircase, seldom used, which leads into the fourth community-room, in the fourth storey. Following the passage just mentioned, you enter by a door—

3rd. A little sitting-room, furnished in the following manner: with chairs, a sofa on the north side, covered with a red-figured cover and fringe; a table in the middle, commonly bearing one or two books, an inkstand, pen, &c. At one corner is a little projection into the room, caused by a staircase leading from above to the floor below, without any communication with the second storey. This room has a door opening upon a staircase leading down to the yard, on the opposite side of which is a gate opening into the cross street. By this way the physician is admitted, except when he comes later than usual. When he comes in, he usually sits a little while, until a nun goes into the adjoining nuns' sick-room, to see if all is ready, and returns to admit him. After prescribing for the patients, he goes no further, but returns by the way he enters; and these are the only rooms into which he is ever admitted.

4th. The nun's sick-room adjoins the little sitting-room on the east, and has, I think, four windows towards the north, with the beds ranged in two rows from end to end, and a few more between them, near the opposite extremity. The door to the sitting-room swings to the left, and behind it is a table, while a glass case on the right contains a wax figure of the infant Saviour, with several sheep. Near the north-eastern corner of this room are two doors, one of which opens into a long and narrow passage, leading to the head of the great staircase that conducts to the cross street. By this passage the physician sometimes finds his way to the sick room, when he comes later than usual. He rings the bell at the gate, which I was told had a concealed pull, known only to him and the priests, proceeds up stairs and through the passage, rapping three times at the door of the sick-room, which is opened by a nun in attendance, after she has given one rap in reply. When he has visited his patients and prescribed for them, he returns by the same way.

5th. Next beyond the sick-room, is a large unoccupied apartment, half divided by two partial partitions, which leave an open space in the middle. Here some of the old nuns commonly meet in the day time.

6th. A door from this apartment opens into another, not appropriated to any particular use, but containing a table, where medicines are sometimes prepared by an old nun, who is usually found there. Passing through this room, you enter a passage, with doors on its four sides; that on the left, which is kept fastened on the inside, leads to the stair-case and gate; and that in front to the private sick-rooms, soon to be described.

7th. That on the right leads to another, appropriated to nuns suffering with the most loathsome disease. There was usually a number of straw mattresses in that room, as I well know, having helped to carry them in, after the yard-man had filled them. A door beyond enters into a store-room, which extends also beyond this apartment. On the right, another door opens into another passage, crossing which, you enter by a door.

8th. A room with bed and screen in one corner, on which nuns were laid to be examined, before their introduction into the sick-room last mentioned. Another door opposite the former, opens into a passage, in which is a staircase leading down.

9th. Beyond this is a spare room, sometimes used to store apples, boxes of different things, &c.

10th. Returning now to the passage which opens on one side upon the stairs to the gate, we enter the only remain-ing door, which leads into an apartment usually occupied by some of the old nuns, and frequently by the Superior.

11th and 12th. Beyond this are two more sick-rooms, in one of which those nuns stay who are waiting their accouchement, and in the other those who have passed it.

13th. The next is a small sitting-room, where a priest waits to baptize the infants previous to their murder. A passage leads from this room on the left, by the doors of two succeeding apartments, neither of which have I ever entered.

14th. The first of them is the 'holy retreat', or room occupied by the priests, while suffering the penalty of their licentiousness.

15th. The other is a sitting-room, to which they have access. Beyond these, the passage leads to two rooms, containing closets for the storage of various articles; and two others, where persons are received who come on business.

The public hospitals succeed, and extend a considerable distance – I believe, to the extremity of the building. By a public entrance in that part, priests often came into the Nunnery; and I have often seen some of them thereabouts, who must have entered that way. Indeed, priests often get into the 'holy retreat', without exposing themselves to the view of persons in the other parts of the Convent, and have been first known to be there, by the yard-nuns being sent to the Seminary for their clothes.

The Congregational Nunnery was founded by a nun, called Sister Bourgeoise. She taught a school in Montreal, and left property for the foundation of a Convent. Her body is buried, and her heart is kept under the Nunnery in an iron chest, which has been shown to me, with the assurance that it continues in perfect preservation, although she has been dead more than one hundred and fifty years. In the chapel is the following inscription: 'Sœur Bourgeoise, Fondatrice du Couvent.' (Sister Bourgeoise, Founder of the Convent).

Nothing was more common than for the Superior to step

hastily into our community-room, while numbers of us were assembled there, and hastily communicate her wishes in words like these:

'Here are the parents of such a novice; come with me, and bear me out in this story.' She would then mention the outlines of a tissue of falsehoods she had just invented, that we might be prepared to fabricate circumstances, and throw in whatever else might favour the deception. This was justified and indeed most highly commanded, by the system of faith by which we are instructed.

It was a common remark always at the initiation of a new nun into the Black nun department, that is, to receive the black veil, that the introduction of another novice into the convent as a veiled nun, always caused the introduction of a veiled nun into heaven as a saint, which was on account of the singular disappearance of some of the older nuns always at the entrance of new ones.

To witness the scenes which often occurred between us and strangers would have struck a person most powerfully, if he had known how truth was set at nought. The Superior, with a serious and dignified air, and a pleasant voice and aspect, would commence a recital of things most favourable to the character of the absent novice, representing her equally fond of her situation, and beloved by the other inmates. The tale told by the Superior, whatever it was, however unheard before might have been any of her statements, was then attested by us, who in every way we could think of, endeavoured to confirm her declarations beyond the reach of doubt.

Sometimes the Superior would entrust the management of such a case to some of the nuns, whether to habituate us to the practice in which she was so highly accomplished, or to relieve herself of what would have been a serious burden to most other persons, or to ascertain whether she could depend upon us—or all together—I cannot tell. I cannot tell. Often, however, have I seen her throw open a door, and say, in a hurried manner, 'Who can tell the best story?'

One point, on which we have received frequent and particular instructions was, the nature of falsehoods. On this subject I have heard many a speech, I had almost said many a sermon; and I was led to believe that it was one of great importance, one on which it was a duty to be well informed, as well as to act. 'What!' exclaimed a priest one day – 'what, a nun of your age, and not know the difference between a wicked and a religious lie!'

He then went on, as had been done many times previously in my hearing, to show the essential difference between the two different kinds of falsehoods. A lie told merely for the injury of another, for our own interest alone, or for no object at all, he painted as a sin worthy of penance. – But a lie told for the good of the church or convent, was meritorious, and of course the telling of it a duty. And of this class of lies there were many varieties and shades. This doctrine has been inculcated on me and my companions in the nunnery, more times than I can enumerate; and to say that it was generally received, would be to tell part of the truth. We often saw the practice of it, and were frequently made to take part in it. Whenever anything which the Superior thought important, could be most conveniently accomplished by falsehood, she resorted to it without scruple.

There was a class of cases in which she more frequently relied on deception than any other.

The friends of novices frequently applied at the Convent to see them, or at least to inquire after their welfare. It was common for them to be politely refused an interview, on some account or other, generally a mere pretext; and then the Superior generally sought to make as favourable an impression as possible on the visitors. Sometimes she would make up a story on the spot, and tell the strangers; requiring some of us to confirm it in the most convincing way we could.

At other times she would prefer to make over to us the task of deceiving, and we were commended in proportion to our ingenuity and success.

Some nun usually showed her submission by immediately stepping forward. She would then add, perhaps, that the parents of such a novice, whom she named, were in waiting, and it was necessary that they should be told such and such things. To perform so difficult a task well, was considered a difficult duty, and it was one of the most certain ways to gain the favour of the Superior. Whoever volunteered to make a story on the spot, was sent immediately to tell it, and the other nuns present were hurried off with her under strict injunctions to uphold her in everything she might state. The Superior, as there was every reason to believe, on all such occasions, when she did not herself appear, hastened to the apartment adjoining that in which the nuns were going, there to listen through the thin partition, to hear whether all performed their parts aright. It was not uncommon for her to go rather further, when she wanted to give such explanations as she could have desired. She would then enter abruptly, and ask, 'Who can tell a good story this morning?' and hurry us off without a moment's delay, to do our best at a venture, without waiting for instructions. It would be curious, could a stranger from the 'wicked world' outside the Convent, witness such a scene. One of the nuns, who felt in a favourable humour to undertake the proposed task, would step promptly forward, and signify her readiness in the usual way, by a knowing wink of one eye, and a slight toss of the head.

'Well, go and do the best you can,' the Superior would say: 'and all the rest of you mind and swear to it.' The latter part of the order, at least, was always performed; for in every case, all the nuns present appeared as unanimous witnesses of everything that was uttered by the spokeswoman of the day.

We were constantly hearing it repeated, that we must never again look upon ourselves as our own; but must remember that we were solely and irrevocably devoted to God. Whatever was required of us, we were called upon to yield under the most solemn considerations. I cannot speak on

every particular with equal freedom: but I wish my readers
clearly to understand the condition in which we were placed,
and the means used to reduce us to what we had to submit
to. Not only were we required to perform the several tasks
imposed upon us at work, prayers, and penances, under
the idea that we were performing solemn duties to our
Maker, but everything else which was required of us, we
were constantly told, was something indispensable in his
sight. The priests, we admitted, were the servants of God,
especially appointed by his authority, to teach us our duty,
to absolve us from sin, and lead us to heaven. Without their
assistance, we had allowed we could never enjoy the favour
of God; unless they administered the sacrament to us, we
could not enjoy everlasting happiness. Having consented to
acknowledge all this, we had no objection to urge against
admitting any other demand that might be made for or by
them. If we thought an act ever so criminal, the Superior
would tell us that the priests acted under the direct sanction
of God, and *could not sin*. Of course, then, it could not be
wrong to comply with any of their requests, because they
could not demand anything but what was right. On the
contrary, to refuse to do anything they asked would necessarily be sinful. Such doctrines admitted, and such practices
performed, it will not seem wonderful when I mention that
we often felt something of their preposterous character.

Sometimes we took pleasure in ridiculing some of the
favourite themes of our teachers; and I recollect one subject
particularly, which at one period afforded us repeated merriment. It may seem irreverent in me to give the account, but
I do it to show how things of a solemn nature were sometimes treated in the convent, by women bearing the title of
saints. A Canadian novice, who spoke very broken English,
one day remarked that she was performing some duty 'for
the God'. This peculiar expression had something ridiculous
to the ears of some of us; and it was soon repeated again
and again, in application to various ceremonies which we
had to perform. Mad Jane Ray seized upon it with avidity,

and with her aid it soon took the place of a by-word in conversation, so that we were constantly reminding each other that we were doing this thing and that thing, how trifling and unmeaning soever, 'for the God'. Nor did we stop here; when the Superior called upon us to bear witness to one of her religious lies, or to fabricate the most spurious one the time would admit; to save her the trouble, we were sure to be reminded, on our way to the stranger's room, that we were doing it 'for the God'. And so it was when other things were mentioned – everything which belonged to our condition was spoken of in somewhat similar terms.

I have hardly detained the reader long enough on this subject to give him a just impression of the stress laid on confession. It is one of the great points to which our attention was constantly directed. We were directed to keep a strict and constant watch over our thoughts; to have continually before our minds the rules of the convent, to compare the one with the other, remember every devotion, and tell all, even the smallest, at confession, either to the Superior or to the priest. My mind was thus kept in a continual state of activity, which proved very wearisome; and it required the constant exertion of our teachers to keep us up to the practice they inculcated.

Another tale recurs to me, of those which were frequently told us, to make us feel the importance of unreserved confession.

A nun of our convent, who had hidden some sin from her confessor, died suddenly, and without any one to confess her. Her sisters assembled to pray for the peace of her soul, when she appeared, and informed them that it would be of no use, but rather troublesome to her, as her pardon was impossible. The doctrine is, that prayers made for souls guilty of unconfessed sin, do but sink them deeper in hell; and this is the reason I have heard given for not praying for Protestants.

The authority of the priests in everything, and the enormity of every act which opposes it, were also impressed upon our minds, in various ways, by our teachers. A 'Father' told us the following story one day at catechism.

A man once died who had failed to pay some money which the priest had asked of him; he was condemned to be burnt in purgatory until he should pay it, but had permission to come back to this world, and take a human body to work in. He made his appearance, therefore, again on earth, and hired himself to a rich man as a labourer. He worked all day, with the fire working in him, unseen by other people: but while he was in bed that night, a girl in an adjoining room, perceiving the smell of brimstone, looked through a crack in the wall, and saw him covered with flames. She informed his master, who questioned him the next morning, and found that his hired man was secretly suffering the pains of purgatory, for neglecting to pay a certain sum of money to the priest. He, therefore, furnished him with the amount due; it was paid, and the servant went off immediately to heaven. The priest cannot forgive any debt due unto him, because it is the Lord's estate.

While at confession, I was urged to hide nothing from the priests, and have been told by them, that they already knew what was in my heart, but would not tell, because it was necessary for me to confess it. I really believed that the priests were acquainted with my thoughts; and often stood in awe of them. They often told me, they had power to strike me dead at any moment.

CHAPTER IX

I FOUND that I had several namesakes among the nuns, for there were two others who had already borne away my new name, Saint Eustace. This was not a solitary case, for there were five Saint Marys, and three Saint Monros, besides two novices of that name. Of my namesakes, I have little to say, for they resembled most nuns; being so much cut off from intercourse with me and other sisters, that I never saw anything in them, nor learnt anything about them, worth mentioning.

Several of my new companions were squaws, who had taken the veil at different times. They were from some of the Indian settlements in the country, but were not distinguishable by any striking habits of character from other nuns, and were generally not very different in their appearance when in their usual dress, and engaged in their customary occupations. It was evident they were treated with much kindness and lenity by the Superior and the old nuns; and this I discovered was done in order to render them as well contented and happy in their situations as possible: and should have attributed the motives for this partiality to their wishing, that they might not influence others to keep away, had I not known they were, like ourselves, unable to exert such an influence. And therefore, I could not satisfy my own mind why this difference was made. Many of the Indians were remarkably devoted to the priests, believing everything they were taught; and as it is represented to be not only a high honour, but a real advantage to a family, to have one of its members become a nun, Indian parents will often pay large sums of money for the admission of their daughters into a convent. The father of one of the squaws, I was told, paid to the Superior nearly her weight in silver on her reception, although he was obliged to sell nearly all his property to raise the money. This he did voluntarily, because he thought himself overpaid by having the advantage of her prayers, self-sacrifices, &c., for himself and the remainder of his family.

The squaws sometimes served to amuse us; for when we were partially dispirited or gloomy, the Superior would occasionally send them to dress themselves in their Indian garments, which usually excited us to merriment.

Among the squaw nuns whom I particularly remember, was one of the Saint Hypolites, not the one who figured in a dreadful scene, described in another part of this narrative, but a woman of a far more mild and humane character.

Three or four days after my reception, the Superior sent me into the cellar for coals; and after she had given me directions, I proceeded down a staircase with a lamp in my hand. I soon found myself on the bare earth in a spacious place, so dark that I could not at once distinguish its form or size, but I observed that it had very solid stone walls, and was arched overhead, at no great elevation. Following my directions, I proceeded onwards from the foot of the stairs, where appeared to be one end of the cellar. After walking about fifteen paces, I passed three small doors, on the right, fastened with large iron bolts on the outside, pushed into posts of stone work, and each having a small opening above, covered with a fine grating, secured by a smaller bolt. On my left were three smaller doors, resembling these, and placed opposite them.

Beyond these, the space became broader: the doors evidently closed small compartments, projecting from the outer wall of the cellar. I soon stepped upon a wooden floor, on which were heaps of wood, coarse linen, and other articles, apparently deposited there for occasional use. I soon crossed the floor, and found the bare earth again under my feet.

A little further on, I found the cellar again contracted in size by a row of closets, or smaller compartments, projecting on each side. These were closed by doors of a different description from the first, having a simple fastening, and no opening through them.

Just beyond, on the left side, I passed a staircase leading up, and then three doors, much resembling those first described, standing opposite three more, on the other side of the cellar. Having passed these, I found the cellar enlarged as before, and here the earth appeared as if mixed with some whitish substance, which attracted my attention.

As I proceeded, I found the whiteness increase, until the surface looked almost like snow, and in a short time I observed before me, a hole dug so deep into the earth that I could perceive no bottom. I stopped to observe it – it was circular, twelve or perhaps fifteen feet across, in the middle of the cellar, and unprotected by any kind of curb, so that one might easily have walked into it in the dark.

The white substance which I have observed, was spread all over the surface around it; and lay in quantities on all sides, that it seemed as if a great deal of it must have been thrown into the hole. It immediately occurred to me that the white substance was lime, and that was the place where the infants were buried, after being murdered, as the superior had informed me. I knew that lime is often used by Roman Catholics in burying places; and in that way I accounted for its being scattered about the spot in such quantities.

This was a shocking thought to me; but I can hardly tell how it affected me, as I had already been prepared to expect dreadful things in the Convent, and had undergone trials which prevented me from feeling as I should formerly have done in similar circumstances.

I passed the spot, therefore, with dreadful thoughts, it is true, about the little corpses which might be in that secret burying place, but with recollections also of the declarations which I had heard, about the favour done their souls in sending them direct to heaven, and the necessary virtue accompanying all the actions of the priests.

Whether I noticed them or not at the time, there is a window or two on each side nearly against the hole, in at which are sometimes thrown articles brought to them from without, for the use of the Convent. Through the window on my right, which opens into the yard, towards the cross street, lime is received from carts; I then saw a large heap of it near the place.

Passing the hole, I came to a spot where was another projection on each side, with three cells like those I first described. Beyond them, in another broad part of the cellar, were heaps of vegetables, and other things, on the right! and on the left, I found the charcoal I was in search of. This was placed in a heap against the wall, as I might then have observed, near a small high window, like the rest, at which it is thrown in. Beyond this spot, at a distance, the cellar terminated.

The top, quite to the point, is arched overhead, though at different heights, for the earth on the bottom is uneven, and in some places several feet higher than in others.

Not liking to be alone in so spacious and gloomy a part of the Convent, especially after the discovery I had made, I hastened to fill my basket with coal, and to return.

Here then I was in a place which I had considered as the nearest imitation of heaven to be found on earth, amongst a society where deeds were constantly perpetrated, which I had believed to be most criminal, and had now found the place in which harmless infants were unfeelingly thrown out of sight, after being murdered.

And yet, such is the power of instruction and example, although not satisfied, as many around me seemed to be, that this was all righteous and proper, I sometimes was half inclined to believe it, for the priests could do no sin, and this was done by priests.

Among the first instructions I received from the Superior, were such as prepared me to admit priests into the nunnery, from the street, at irregular hours. It is no secret that priests enter and go out; but if they were to be watched by any person in St. Paul's Street all day long, no irregularity might be suspected; and they might be supposed to visit the Convent for the performance of religious ceremonies merely.

But if a person were near the gate about midnight, he might sometimes form a different opinion; for when a stray priest is shut out of the Seminary, or is otherwise put in the need of seeking a lodging, he is always sure of being admitted into the Black Nunnery. Nobody but a priest can ever ring the bell at the sick-room door; much less can any but a priest gain admittance. The pull of the bell is entirely concealed, somewhere on the outside of the gate, I have been told.

He makes himself known as a priest by a peculiar kind of hissing sound, made by the tongue against the teeth while they are kept closed and the lips open. The nun within, who delays to open the door until informed what kind of an applicant is there, immediately recognizes the signal, and replies with two inarticulate sounds, such as are often used instead of yes, with the mouth closed.

The Superior seemed to consider this part of my instructions quite important, and taught me the signals. I had often occasion to use them; I have been repeatedly called to the door, in the night, while watching in the sick-room; and on reaching it, heard the short hissing sound I have mentioned; then, according to my standing orders, unfastened the door, admitted a priest, who was at liberty to go where he pleased. I will name M. Bierze, from St. Denis.

The books used in the nunnery, at least such as I recollect of them, were the following. Most of these are lecture books, or such as are used by the daily readers, while we were at work and meals. These were all furnished by the Superior, out of her library, to which we never had access. She was informed when we had done with the book, and then exchanged it for another, as she pleased to select.

Le Miroir du Chrétien (Christian Mirror), History of Rome, History of the Church, Life of Soeur Bourgeoise, (the founder of the Convent), in two volumes, L'Ange Conducteur, (the Guardian Angel), L'Ange Chrétien (the Christian Angel), Les Vies des Saints, (Lives of the Saints), in several volumes, Dialogues, a volume consisting of conversations between a Protestant Doctor, called Dr. D., and a Catholic gentleman, on the articles of faith, in which, after much ingenious reasoning, the former was confuted; one large book, the name of which I have forgotten, occupied us nine or ten months at our lectures, night and morning, L'Instruction de la Jeunesse, (the Instruction of Youth), containing much about Convents, and the education of persons in the world, with a great deal on confessions, &c.

Examen de la Conscience (Examination of Conscience), is a book frequently used.

I may here remark, that I never saw a Bible in the Convent from the day I entered as a novice, until that on which I effected my escape. The Catholic New Testament, commonly called the Evangile, was read to us about three or four times a year. The Superior directed the reader what passage to select; but we never had it in our hands to read when we pleased. I often heard the Protestant Bible spoken of, in bitter terms, as a most dangerous book, and one which never ought to be in the hands of common people.

CHAPTER X

LARGE quantities of bread are made in the Black Nunnery every week, for, besides what is necessary to feed the nuns, many of the poor are supplied. When a priest wishes to give a loaf of bread to a poor person, he gives him an order, which is presented at the Convent. The making of bread is, therefore, one of the most laborious employments in the institution.

The manufacture of wax candles was another important branch of business in the nunnery. It was carried on in a small room, on the first floor, thence called the ciergerie, or candle-room, cierge being the word for wax candle. I was sometimes sent to read the daily lecture and catechism to the nuns employed there, but found it a very unpleasant task, as the smell rising from the melted wax gave me a sickness at the stomach. The employment was considered as rather unhealthy, and those were assigned to it who had the strongest constitutions. The nuns who were more employed in that room were Saint Maria, Saint Catherine, Saint Charlotte, Saint Hyacinthe, Saint Hypolite, and others. But with these, as with other persons in the Convent, I was never allowed to speak, except under circumstances before mentioned. I was sent to read, and was not allowed even to answer the most trivial question, if one were asked me. Should a nun say, 'What o'clock is it?' I never should have dared to reply, but was required to report her to the Superior.

Much stress was laid on the sainte scapulaire, or holy scapulary. This is a small band of cloth or silk, formed and wrought in a particular manner, to be tied around the neck, by two strings, fastened to the ends. I have made many of them, having been sometimes set to make them in the Convent. On one side is worked a kind of double cross (thus, XX), and on the other, I. H. S., the meaning of which I do not exactly know. Such a band is called a scapulary, and many miracles are attributed to its power. Children on first receiving the communion are often presented with scapularies, which they are taught to regard with great reverence. We were told of the wonders effected by their means, in the addresses that were made to us, by priests, at catechisms or lectures. I will repeat one or two of the stories which occur to me.

A Roman Catholic servant woman, who had concealed some of her sins at confession, acted so hypocritical a part as to make her mistress believe her a *devotee*, or strict observer of her duty. She even imposed upon her confessor to such a degree that he gave her a scapulary. After he had given it, however, one of the saints in heaven informed him in a vision, that the holy scapulary must not remain on the neck of so great a sinner, and that it must be restored to the church. She lay down that night with the scapulary round her throat; but in the morning was found dead, with her head cut off, and the scapulary was discovered in the church. The belief was, that the devil could not endure to have so holy a thing on one of his servants, and had pulled so hard to get it off, as to draw the silken thread, with which it was tied, through her neck; after which, by some divine power, it was restored to the church.

Another story was as follows. A poor Roman Catholic

was once taken prisoner by the heretics. He had a sainte scapularie on his neck, when God, seeing him in the midst of his foes, took it from the neck by a miracle, and held it up in the air above the throng of heretics; more than one hundred of whom were converted, by seeing it thus supernaturally suspended.

I had been informed by the Superior, on my first admission as a nun, that there was a subterraneous passage, leading from the cellar of our Convent, into that of the Congregational Nunnery: but, though I had so often visited the cellar, I had never seen it. One day, after I had been received three or four months, I was sent to walk through it on my knees, with another nun, as a penance. This, and other penances, were sometimes put upon us by the priests, without any reason assigned. The common way, indeed, was to tell us of the sin for which a penance was imposed, but we were left many times to conjecture. Now and then the priest would inform us at a subsequent confession, when he happened to recollect something about it, as I thought, and not because he reflected or cared much upon the subject.

The nun who was with me led through the cellar, passing to the right of the secret burial-place, and showed me the door of the subterraneous passage, which was at the extremity towards the Congregational Nunnery. The reasons why I had not noticed it before, I presume, were, that it was made to shut close and even with the wall: and all that part of the cellar was white-washed. The door, which is of wood, and square, opens with a latch into a passage about four feet and a half high. We immediately got upon our knees, commenced saying the prayers required, and began to move slowly along the dark and narrow passage. It may be fifty or sixty feet in length. When we reached the end, we opened a door, and found ourselves in the cellar of the Congregational Nunnery, at some distance from the outer wall; for the covered way is carried on towards the middle of the cellar by two low partitions covered at the top. By the

side of the door was placed a list of names of the Black
Nuns, with a slide that might be drawn over any of them.
We covered our names in this manner, as evidence of having
performed the duty assigned us; and then returned down-
wards on our knees, by the way we had come. This penance
I repeatedly performed afterwards; and by this way, as I
have occasion elsewhere to mention, nuns from the Congregational Nunnery sometimes entered our Convent for
worse purposes.

We were frequently assured that miracles are still performed; and pains were taken to impress us deeply on this
subject. The Superior often spoke to us of the Virgin Mary's
pincushion, the remains of which are pretended to be preserved in the Convent, though it has crumbled quite to dust.
We regarded this relic with such veneration, that we were
afraid even to look at it, and we often heard the following
story related, when the subject was introduced.

A priest in Jerusalem once had a vision, in which he was
informed that the house in which the Virgin had lived,
should be removed from its foundations, and transported to
a distance. He did not think the communication was from
God, and therefore disregarded it; but the house was soon
after missed, which convinced him that the vision was true,
and he told where the house might be found. A picture of
the house is preserved in the Nunnery, and was sometimes
shown us. There were also wax figures of Joseph sawing
wood, and Jesus, as a child, picking up the chips. We were
taught to sing a little song relating to this, the chorus of
which I remember:

> 'Saint Josèph Charpentier,
> Petit Jesus ramassait les corpeaux
> Pour faire bouillir la marmite!'

(St. Joseph was a carpenter, little Jesus collected chips to
make the pot boil.)

I began to speak of miracles, and I recollect a story of
one, about a family in Italy saved from shipwreck by a

priest, who were in consequence converted, and had two
sons honoured with the priest's office.

I had heard, before I entered the Convent, about a great
fire which had destroyed a number of houses in the Quebec
suburbs, and which some said the Bishop extinguished with
holy water. I once heard a Catholic and a Protestant
disputing on this subject, and when I went to the Congregational Nunnery, I sometimes heard the children, alluding
to the same story, say, at an alarm of fire, 'Is it a Catholic
fire? Then why does not the Bishop run?'

Among the topics on which the Bishop addressed the
nuns in the Convent, this was one. He told us the story one
day, that he could have sooner interfered and stopped the
flames, but that at last, finding they were about to destroy
too many Catholic houses, he threw holy water on the fire,
and extinguished it. I believed this, and also thought that
he was able to put out any fire, but that he never did it except
when inspired.

The holy water which the Bishop has consecrated, was
considered much more efficacious than any blessed by a
common priest; and this it was which was used in the Convent in sprinkling our beds. It has a virtue in it, to keep off
any evil spirit.

Now that I was a nun, I was occasionally sent to read
lectures to the novices, as other nuns had been while I was a
novice. There were but few of us who were thought capable
of reading English well enough, and, therefore, I was more
frequently sent than I might otherwise have been. The
Superior often said to me, as I was going among the novices:

'Try to convert them – save their souls – you know you
will have a higher place in heaven for every one you convert.'

For whatever reason, Mad Jane Ray seemed to take
great delight in crossing and provoking the Superior and
old nuns; and often she would cause an interruption when it
was most inconvenient and displeasing to them. The preservation of silence was insisted upon most rigidly, and
penances of such a nature were imposed for breaking it,

that it was a constant source of uneasiness with me, to know that I might infringe the rules in so many ways, and that inattention might at any moment subject me to something very unpleasant. During the periods of meditation, therefore, and those of lecture, work, and repose, I kept a strict guard upon myself, to escape penances, as well as to avoid sin; and the silence of the others convinced me that they were equally watchful, and from the same motives.

My feelings, however, varied at different times, and so did those of many, if not of all my companions, excepting the older ones, who took their turns in watching us. We sometimes felt indisposed for gaiety, and threw off all idea that talking was sinful, even when required by the rules of the Convent. I even, when I felt that I might perhaps be doing wrong, reflected that confession, and certainly penance, would soon wipe off the guilt.

I may remark here, that I ere long found out several things important to be known to a person living under such rules. One of these was, that it was much better to confess to a priest a sin committed against the rules, because he would not require one of the penances I most disliked, viz., those which exposed me to the observation of the nuns, or which demanded self-debasement before them, like begging their pardon, kissing the floor, or the Superior's feet, &c., and, besides, he as a confessor was bound to secrecy, and could not inform the Superior against me. My conscience being as effectually unburdened by my confession to the priest, as I had been taught to believe, I therefore preferred not to tell my sins to any one else: and this course I found was preferred by others for the same good reasons.

To Jane Ray, however, it sometimes appeared to be a matter of perfect indifference, who knew her violations of rule, to what penance she exposed herself.

Often and often, while perfect silence prevailed among the nuns, at meditation, or while nothing was to be heard except the voice of the reader appointed for the day, no matter whose life or writings were presented for our contemplation, Jane would break forth with some remark or question, that would attract general attention, and often cause a long and total interruption. Sometimes she would make some harmless remark or inquiry aloud, as if through mere inadvertency, and then her loud and well-known voice, so strongly associated with everything singular and ridiculous, would arrest the attention of us all, and generally incline us to laugh. The Superior would then usually utter some hasty remonstrance, and many a time I have heard her pronounce some penance upon her; but Jane had some apology ready, or some reply calculated to irritate still further, or to prove to every one that no punishment would be effectual on her. Sometimes this singular woman would appear to be actuated by opposite feelings and motives; for although she usually delighted in drawing others into difficulty, and has thrown many a severe penance even upon her greatest favourites, on other occasions she appeared totally regardless of consequences herself, and preferred to take all the blame, anxious only to shield others.

I have repeatedly known her to break silence in the community, as if she had no object, or none beyond that of causing disturbance, or exciting a smile, and as soon as it was noticed, exclaim, 'Say it's me, say it's me!'

Sometimes she would even expose herself to punishment in place of another who was guilty; and thus I found it difficult fully to understand her. In some cases she seemed decidedly out of her wits, as the Superior and priests commonly preferred to represent her; but generally I saw in her what prevented me from accounting her insane.

Among her common tricks were such as these; she gave me the name of the 'Devout English Reader', because I was often appointed to read the lecture to the English girls; and sometimes, after taking a seat near me, under pretence of deafness, would whisper it in my hearing, because she knew my want of self-command when excited to laughter. Thus she often exposed me to penances for a breach of decorum, and set me to biting my lips, to avoid laughing outright in the midst of a solemn lecture. 'Oh! you devout English reader!' would sometimes come upon me suddenly from her lips, with something in it so ludicrous, that I had to exert myself to the utmost to avoid observation.

This came so often at one time, that I grew uneasy, and told her I must confess it, to unburden my conscience. I had not done so before, because she would complain of me, for giving way to temptation.

Sometimes she would pass behind us as we stood at dinner ready to sit down, and softly moving back our chairs, leave us to fall down upon the floor. This she has repeatedly done; and while we were laughing together, she would spring forward, kneel to the Superior, and beg her pardon and a penance.

CHAPTER XI

But I must now come to one deed in which I had some part, and which I look back upon with greater horror and pain than any occurrences in the Convent, in which I was not the principal sufferer. It is not necessary for me to attempt to excuse myself in this or any other case. Those who have any disposition to judge fairly, will exercise their own judgment in making allowances for me, under the fear and force, the command and examples, before me. I, therefore, shall confine myself, as usual, to the simple narration of facts. The time was about five months after I took the veil, the weather was cool, perhaps in September or October. One day the Superior sent for me and several other nuns, to receive her commands at a particular room. We found the Bishop and some priests with her; and speaking in an unusual tone of fierceness and authority, she said, 'Go to the room for the Examination of Conscience, and drag St. Frances upstairs.' Nothing more was necessary than this unusual command, with the tone and manner which accompanied it, to excite in me the most gloomy anticipations. It did not strike me as strange that St. Frances should be in the room to which the Superior directed us. It was an apartment to which we were often sent to prepare for the communion, and to which we voluntarily went, whenever we felt the compunctions which our ignorance of duty, and the misinstructions we received, inclined us to seek relief from self-reproach. Indeed I had seen her there a little before. What terrified me was, first, the Superior's angry manner; second, the expression she used, being a French term, whose peculiar use I had learnt in the Convent, and whose meaning is rather softened when translated into *drag*; third, the place to which we were directed to take the interesting young nun, and the persons assembled there, as I supposed, to condemn her. My fears were such, concerning the fate that awaited her, and my horror at the idea that she was in some way to be sacrificed, that I would have given anything to be allowed to stay where I was. But I feared the consequences of disobeying the Superior, and proceeded with the rest towards the room for the examination of conscience.

The room to which we were to proceed from that, was in the second story, and the place of many a scene of a shameful nature. It is sufficient to say, after what I have said in other parts of this book, that things had there occurred which made me regard the place with the greatest disgust. Saint Frances had appeared melancholy for some time. I well knew that she had cause, for she had been repeatedly subject to trials which I need not name – our common lot. When we reached the room where we had been bidden to seek her, I entered the door, my companions standing behind me, as the place was so small as hardly to hold five persons at a time. The young nun was standing alone, near the middle of the room; she was probably about twenty, with light hair, blue eyes, and a very fair complexion. I spoke to her in a compassionate voice, but at the same time with such a decided manner, that she comprehended my meaning.

'Saint Frances, we are sent for you.'

Several others spoke kindly to her, but two addressed her very harshly. The poor creature turned round with a look of meekness, and without expressing any unwillingness or fear, without even speaking a word, resigned herself to our hands. The tears came into my eyes. I had not a moment's doubt that she considered her fate as sealed, and was already beyond the fear of death. She was conducted or rather hurried to the staircase, which was near by, and then seized by her limbs and clothes, and in fact almost dragged upstairs, in the sense the Superior had intended. I laid my own hands upon her – I took hold of her, too, more gently indeed than some of the rest; yet I encouraged and assisted them in carrying her. I could not avoid it. My refusal would not have saved her, nor prevented her from being carried up; it would only have exposed me to some severe punishment, as I believe some of my companions would have seized the first opportunity to complain of me.

All the way up the staircase, Saint Frances spoke not a word, nor made the slightest resistance. When we entered, with her, the room to which she was ordered, my heart sank within me. The Bishop, the Lady Superior, and five priests, viz.: Bonin, Richards, Savage, and two others, I now ascertained, were assembled for trial, on some charge of great importance.

When we had brought our prisoner before them, Father Richards began to question her, and she made ready, but calm replies. I cannot pretend to give a connected account of what ensued; my feelings were wrought up to such a pitch, that I knew not what I did, or what to do. I was under a terrible apprehension that, if I betrayed the feelings which overcame me, I should fall under the displeasure of the cold-blooded persecutors of my poor innocent sister; and this fear on the one hand, with the distress I felt for her on the other, rendered me almost frantic. As soon as I entered the room, I had stepped into a corner, on the left of the entrance, where I might partially support myself by leaning against the wall between the door and the window. This support was all that prevented me falling to the floor, for the confusion of my thoughts was so great, that only a few words I heard spoken on either side made any lasting impression upon me. I felt as if struck with some insupportable blow; and death would not have been more frightful to me. I am inclined to the belief that Father Richards wished to shield the poor prisoner from the severity of her fate, by drawing from her expressions that might bear a favourable construction. He asked her, among other things, if she was now sorry for what she had been overheard to say, (for she had been betrayed by one of the nuns), and if she would not prefer confinement in the cells to the punishment which was threatened. But the Bishop soon interrupted him, and it was easy to perceive, that he considered her fate as sealed, and was determined she should not escape. In reply to some of the questions put to her, she was silent; to others I heard her voice reply that she did not repent of words she had uttered, though they had been reported by some of the nuns who had heard them; that she had firmly resolved to resist every attempt to compel her to the commission of crimes which she detested. She added that she would rather die than cause the murder of harmless babes.

'That is enough, finish her!' said the Bishop.

Two nuns instantly fell upon the woman, and in obedience to directions, given by the Superior, prepared to execute her sentence.

She still maintained all the calmness and submission of a lamb. Some of those who took part in this transaction, I believe, were as unwilling as myself: but of others I can safely say, I believe, they delighted in it. Their conduct certainly exhibited a most blood-thirsty spirit. But above all others present, and above all human fiends I ever saw, I think Saint Hypolite was the most diabolical; she engaged in the horrid task with all alacrity, and assumed from choice the most revolting parts to be performed. She seized a gag, forced it into the mouth of the poor nun, and when it was fixed between her extended jaws, so as to keep them open at their greatest possible distance, took hold of the straps fastened at each end of the stick, crossed them behind the helpless head of the victim, and drew them tight through the loop prepared as a fastening.

The bed which had always stood in one part of the room, still remained there; though the screen, which had usually been placed before it, and was made of thick muslin, with only a crevice through which a person might look out, had been folded up on its hinges in the form of a W, and placed in a corner. On the bed the prisoner was laid with her face upwards, and then bound with cords so that she could not move. In an instant, another bed was thrown upon her. One of the priests, named Bonin, sprung like a fury first upon it, with all his force. He was speedily followed by the nuns, until there were as many upon the bed as could find room, and all did what they could, not only to smother, but to bruise her. Some stood up and jumped upon the poor girl with their feet, some with their knees; and others, in different ways, seemed to seek how they might best beat the breath out of her body, and mangle it, without coming in direct contact with it, or seeing the effects of their violences. During this time, my feelings were almost too strong to be endured. I felt stupefied, and scarcely was conscious of what I did. Still, fear for myself remained in a sufficient degree to induce me to some exertion; and I attempted to talk to those who stood next, partly that I might have an excuse for turning away from the dreadful scene.

After the lapse of fifteen or twenty minutes, and when it was presumed that the sufferer had been smothered and crushed to death, Father Bonin and the nuns ceased to trample upon her, and stepped from the bed. All was motionless and silent beneath it.

They then began to laugh at such inhuman thoughts as
occurred to some of them, rallying each other in the most
unfeeling manner, and ridiculing me for feelings which I in
vain endeavoured to conceal. They alluded to the resigna-
tion of our murdered companion; and one of them taunt-
ingly said, 'She would have made a good Catholic martyr.'
After spending some moments in such conversation, one of
them asked if the corpse should be removed. The Superior
said it had better remain a little while. After waiting a short
time longer, the feather-bed was taken off, the cords un-
loosed, and the body taken by the nuns and dragged down
stairs. I was informed that it was taken into the cellar, and
thrown unceremoniously into the hole which I have already
described, covered with a great quantity of lime; and afterwards sprinkled with a liquid, of the properties and name of
which I am ignorant. This liquid I have seen poured into
the hole from large bottles, after the necks were broken off;
and have heard that it is used in France to prevent the
effluvia rising from cemeteries.

I did not soon recover from the shock caused by this
scene; indeed, it still recurs to me, with most gloomy impressions. The next day there was a melancholy aspect over
everything, and recreation time passed in the dullest
manner; scarcely anything was said above a whisper. I never
heard much said afterwards about Saint Frances.

I spoke with one of the nuns, a few words, one day, but
we were all cautioned not to expose ourselves very far, and
could not place much reliance in each other. The murdered
nun had been brought to her shocking end through the
treachery of one of our number in whom she confided.

I never knew with certainty who had reported her
remarks to the Superior, but suspicion fastened on one, and
I never could regard her but with detestation.

I was more inclined to blame her than some of those employed in the execution; for there could have been no
necessity for the betrayal of her feelings. We all knew how
to avoid exposing each other.

I was often sent by the Superior to overhear what was said by novices and nuns, when they seemed to shun her; she would say, 'Go and listen, they are speaking English'; and though I obeyed her, I never informed her against them. If I wished to clear my conscience, I would go to a priest and confess, knowing that he dared not communicate what I said to any person, and that he would not choose as heavy penances as the Superior.

We were always at liberty to choose another confessor when we had any sin to confess, which we were unwilling to tell one to whom we should otherwise have done.

Not long after the murder just related, a young woman came to the nunnery, and asked for permission to see St. Frances. It was my former friend, with whom I had been an assistant teacher, Miss Louisa Boquet, of St. Denis. From this, I supposed the murdered nun might have come from that town, or its vicinity. The only answer was, that St. Frances was dead.

Some time afterwards, some of St. Frances' friends called to inquire after her, and they were told that she had died a glorious death; and further told, that she made some heavenly expressions, which were repeated in order to satisfy her friends.

CHAPTER XII

THE pictures in the room of the three states were large, and painted by some artist who understood how to make some horrible ones. They appeared to be stuck to the walls. The light is admitted from small and high windows, which are curtained, and is rather faint, so as to make everything look gloomy. The story told us was, that they were painted by an artist, to whom God had given power to represent things exactly as they are in heaven, hell, and purgatory.

In heaven, the picture of which hangs on one side of

the apartment, multitudes of nuns and priests are put in the highest places, with the Virgin Mary at their head, St. Peter and other saints, far above the great numbers of good Catholics of other classes, who are crowded in below.

In purgatory are multitudes of people; and in one part, called 'The place of lambs', are infants who died unbaptized. 'The place of darkness' is that part of purgatory in which adults are collected, and there they are surrounded by flames, waiting to be delivered by the prayers of the living.

In hell, the picture of which, and that of purgatory, were on the wall opposite that of heaven, the human faces were the most horrible that can be imagined. Persons of different descriptions were represented, with the most distorted features, ghastly complexions, and every variety of dreadful expression; some with wild beasts gnawing at their heads, others furiously biting the iron bars which kept them in, with looks which could not fail to make a spectator shudder.

I could hardly persuade myself that the figures were not living, and the impression they made on my feelings was powerful. I was often shown the place where nuns go who break their vows, as a warning. It is the hottest place in hell, and worse, in every point of view, even than that to which all Protestants are assigned; because they are not so much to be blamed, as we were sometimes assured, as their ministers and the Bible, by which they are perverted.

Whenever I was shut in that room, as I was several times, I prayed for 'les âmes des fidèles trépassés'; the souls of those faithful ones who have long been in purgatory, and have no relations living to pray for them.

My feelings were often of the most painful description, while I remained alone with those frightful pictures.

Jane Ray was once put in, and uttered the most dreadful shrieks. Some of the old nuns proposed to the Superior to have her gagged; 'No,' she replied, 'go and let out that devil, she makes me sin more than all the rest.'

Jane could not endure the place; and she afterwards gave names to many of the worst figures of the pictures. On catechism-days she would take a seat behind a cupboard door, where the priest could not see her, while she faced the nuns, and would make us laugh. 'You are not so attentive to your lessons as you used to be,' he would begin to say, while we were endeavouring to suppress our laughter.

Jane would then hold up the first letter of some priest's name whom she had before compared with one of the faces in 'hell,' and so look that we could hardly preserve our gravity.

I remember she named the wretch who was biting at the bars of hell, with a serpent gnawing his head, with chains and padlocks on, Father Dufresne; and she would say – 'Does he not look like him, when he comes in to catechism with his long solemn face, and begins his speeches with, "My children, my hope is that you have lived very devout lives?" '

The first time I went to confession after taking the veil, I found abundant evidence that the priests did not treat even that ceremony, which is called a solemn sacrament, with respect enough to lay aside the shameless character they so often showed on other occasions. The confessor sometimes sat in the room for the examination of conscience, and sometimes in the Superior's room, and was alone except for the nun who was confessing. He had a common chair placed in the middle of the floor, and instead of being placed behind a grate, or lattice, as in the chapel, had nothing before or around him. There were no spectators to observe him, and of course any such thing would have been unnecessary.

A number of nuns usually confessed on the same day, but only one could be admitted into the room at a time. They took their places just without the door, on their knees, and went through the preparation prescribed by the rules of confession; repeating certain prayers, which always occupy a considerable time. When one was ready, she rose from her knees, entered, and closed the door behind her; and no-one even dared touch the latch till she came out.

I shall not tell what was transacted at such times, under the pretence of confessing, and receiving absolution from sin; far more sin was often incurred than pardoned; and crimes of a deep dye were committed, while trifling irregularities in childish ceremonies, were treated as serious offences. I cannot persuade myself to speak plainly on such a subject, as I must offend the virtuous ear. I can only say, that suspicion cannot do any injustice to the priests, because their sins cannot be exaggerated.

Some idea may be formed of the manner in which even such women as many of my sister nuns, regarded the father confessors, when I state that there was often a contest among us, to avoid entering the apartment as long as we could; endeavouring to make each other go first, as that was what most of us dreaded.

During the long and tedious days which filled up the time between the occurrences I have mentioned, nothing or little took place to keep up our spirits. We were fatigued in body with labour, or with sitting, debilitated by the long continuance of our religious exercises, and depressed in feelings by our miserable and hopeless condition. Nothing but the humours of mad Jane Ray could rouse us for a moment from our languor and melancholy.

To mention all her devices, would require more room than is here allowed, and a memory of almost all her words and actions for years. I had early become a favourite with her, and had opportunity to learn more of her character than most of the other nuns. As this may be learned from hearing what she did, I will here recount a few of her tricks, just as they happen to present themselves to my memory, with regard to the order of time.

She one day, in an unaccountable humour, sprinkled the floor plentifully with holy water, which brought upon her a severe lecture from the Superior, as might have been expected. The Superior said it was a heinous offence; she had wasted holy water enough to save many souls from purgatory; and what would they not give for it. She then ordered Jane to sit in the middle of the floor, and when the priest came, he was informed of her offence. Instead, however, of imposing one of those penances to which she had been subjected, but with so little effect, he said to her, 'Go to your place, Jane; we forgive you for this time.'

I was once set to iron aprons with Jane; aprons and pocket-handkerchiefs are the only articles of dress which are ever ironed in the Convent. As soon as we were alone, she remarked, 'Well, we are free from the rules while we are at this work'; and, although she knew she had no reason for saying so, she began to sing, and I soon joined her, and thus we spent the time, while we were at work, to the neglect of the prayers that we ought to have said.

We had no idea that we were in danger of being overheard, but it happened that the Superior was overhead all the time, with several nuns, who were preparing for confession; she came down and said, 'How is this?' Jane Ray coolly replied that we had employed our time in singing hymns, and referred to me. I was afraid to confirm so direct a falsehood, in order to deceive the Superior, though I had often told more injurious ones of her fabrication, or at her orders, and said very little in reply to Jane's request.

The Superior plainly saw the trick that was attempted, and ordered us both to the room for the examination of conscience, where we remained till night without a mouthful to eat. The time was not, however, unoccupied; I received such a lecture from Jane as I have very seldom heard, and she was so angry with me, that we did not speak to each other for two weeks.

At length she found something to complain of against me, had me subjected to a penance, which led to our begging each other's pardon, and we became perfectly satisfied, reconciled, and as good friends as ever.

One of the most disgusting penances we had ever to submit to, was that of drinking the water in which the Superior

had washed her feet. Nobody could ever laugh at this
penance except Jane Ray. She would pretend to comfort us,
by saying she was sure it was better than mere plain clear
water.

Some of the tricks which I remember, were played by
Jane with nuns' clothes. It was a rule that the oldest aprons
in use should go to the youngest received, and that the old
nuns were to wear all the new ones. On four different occasions, Jane stole into the sleeping-room at night, and unobserved by the watch, changed a great part of the aprons,
placing them by the beds of nuns to whom they did not
belong. The consequence was, that in the morning they
dressed themselves in such haste, as never to discover the
mistake they made, until they were all ranged at prayers;
and then the ridiculous appearance which many of them
cut, disturbed the long devotions. I laugh so easy that, on
such occasions, I usually incurred a full share of penances.
I generally, however, got a new apron, when Jane played
this trick, for it was part of her object to give the best
aprons to her favourites, and put off the ragged ones on some
of the old nuns whom she most hated.

Jane once lost her pocket-handkerchief. The penance for
such an offence is, to go without any for five weeks. For this
she had no relish, and requested me to pick one from some
of the nuns on the way upstairs. I succeeded in getting two;
this Jane said was one too many, and she thought it
dangerous for either of us to keep it, lest a search should be
made. Very soon the two nuns were complaining that they
had lost their handkerchiefs, and wondering what could
have become of them, as they were sure they had been care-
ful. Jane seized an opportunity, and slipped one into a straw
bed, where it remained until the bed was emptied to be filled
with new straw.

As the winter was coming on, one year, she complained
to me that we were not as well supplied with warm night-
clothes, as two of the nuns she named, whom she said she
'abominated.' She soon after found means to get possession

of their fine warm flannel night-gowns, one of which she gave to me, while the other was put on at bedtime. She presumed the owners would have a secret search for them; and in the morning hid them in the stove, after the fire had gone out, which was kindled a little before the hour of rising, and then suffered to burn down.

This she did every morning, taking them out at night through the winter. The poor nuns who owned the garments were afraid to complain of their loss, lest they should have some penance laid on them, and nothing was ever said about them. When the weather began to grow warm in the spring, Jane returned the night-gowns to the beds of the nuns from whom she had borrowed them, and they were probably as much surprised to find them again, as they had been before at losing them.

Jane once found an opportunity to fill her apron with a quantity of fine apples, called *fameuses*, which came in her way, and hastening up to the sleeping-room, hid them under my bed. Then coming down, she informed me, and we agreed to apply for leave to make our elevens, as it is called. The meaning of this is, to repeat a certain round of prayers, for nine days in succession, to some saint we choose to address for assistance in becoming more charitable, affectionate, or something else. We easily obtained permission, and hastened upstairs to begin our nine days' feast on the apples; when, much to our surprise, they had all been taken away, and there was no way to avoid the disagreeable fate we had brought upon ourselves. Jane, therefore, began to search the beds of the other nuns; but not finding any trace of the apples, she became doubly vexed, and stuck pins in those that belonged to her enemies.

When bed-time came, they were much scratched in getting into bed, which made them break silence, and subjected them to penances.

CHAPTER XIII

ONE night, Jane, who had been sweeping the sleeping-room for a penance, dressed up the broomstick, when she had completed her work, with a white cloth on the end, so tied as to resemble an old woman dressed in white, with long arms sticking out. This she stuck through a broken pane of glass, and placed it so that it appeared to be looking in at the window, by the font of holy water. There it remained till the nuns came up to bed. The first who stopped at the font, to dip her finger in, caught a glimpse of the singular object, and started with terror. The next was equally terrified, as she approached, and the next, and the next.

We all believed in ghosts; and it was not wonderful that such an object should cause alarm, especially as it was but a short time after the death of one of the nuns. Thus they went on, each getting a fright in turn, yet all afraid to speak. At length, one more alarmed, or with less presence of mind than the rest, exclaimed, 'Oh, mon Dieu! je ne me coucherai pas!' When the night watch called out, 'Who's that?' she confessed she had broken silence, but pointed at the cause; and when all the nuns assembled at a distance from the window, Jane offered to advance boldly, and ascertain the nature of the apparition, which they thought a most resolute intention. We all stood looking on, when she stepped to the window, drew in the broomstick, and showed us the ridiculous puppet which had alarmed so many superstitious fears.

Some of her greatest feats she performed as a sleep-walker. Whether she ever walked in her sleep or not, I am unable, with certainty, to say. She, however, often imposed upon the Superior, and old nuns, by making them think so, when I knew she did not; and yet I cannot positively say that she never did. I have remarked that one of the old nuns was always placed in our sleeping-room at night, to watch us. Sometimes she would be inattentive, and sometimes fall into a doze. Jane Ray often seized such times to rise from her bed, and walk about, occasionally seizing one of the nuns in bed, in order to frighten her. This she generally effected; and many times we have been awakened by screams of terror. In our alarm, some of us frequently broke silence, and gave occasion to the Superior to lay us under penances. Many times, however, we escaped with a mere reprimand, while Jane usually received expressions of compassion: 'Poor creature; she would not do so if she were in perfect possession of her reason.' And Jane displayed her customary artfulness, in keeping up the false impression. As soon as she perceived that the old nun was likely to observe her, she would throw her arms about, or appear unconscious of what she was doing; falling upon a bed, or standing stock-still, until exertions had been made to rouse her from her supposed lethargy.

We were once allowed to drink cider at dinner, which was quite an extraordinary favour. Jane, however, on account of her negligence of all work, was denied the privilege, which she much resented. The next day, when dinner arrived, we began to taste our new drink, but it was so salt we could not swallow it. Those of us who first discovered it were as usual afraid to speak; but we set down our cups, and looked around, till the others made the same discovery, which they all soon did, and most of them in the same manner. Some, however, at length, taken by surprise, uttered some ludicrous exclamation, on tasting the salted cider, and then an old nun, looking across, would cry out—

'Ah! tu casses lae silence.' (Ah; you've broken silence.)

And thus we soon got a-laughing, beyond our power of supporting it. At recreation that day, the first question asked by many of us was, 'How did you like your cider?'

Jane Ray never had a fixed place to sleep in. When the weather began to grow warm in the spring, she usually pushed some bed out of its place, near a window, and put her own beside it; and when the winter approached, she would choose a spot near the stove, and occupy it with her bed, in spite of all remonstrance. We were all convinced that it was generally best to yield to her.

She was often set to work in different ways; but, whenever she was dissatisfied with doing anything, would devise some trick that would make the Superior or old nuns drive her off; and whenever any suspicion was expressed of her being in her right mind, she would say that she did not know what she was doing; and all the difficulty arose from her repeating prayers too much, which wearied and distracted her mind.

I was once directed to assist Jane Ray in shifting the beds of the nuns. When we came to those of some of the sisters whom she most disliked, she said, 'Now we will pay them for some of the penances we have suffered on their account', and taking some thistles, she mixed them with the straw. At night, the first of them that got into bed felt the thistles, and cried out. The night-watch exclaimed as usual. 'You are breaking silence there.' And then another screamed as she was scratched by the thistles, and another. The old nun then called on all who had broken silence to rise, and ordered them to sleep under their beds as a penance, which they silently complied with. Jane and I afterwards confessed, when it was all over, and took some trifling penance which the priest imposed.

Those nuns who fell most under the displeasure of mad Jane Ray, as I have intimated before, were those who had the reputation of being most ready to inform of the most trifling faults of others, and especially those who acted without any regard to honour, by disclosing what they had pretended to listen to in confidence. Several of the worst-tempered 'saints' she held in abhorrence; and I have heard her say, that such and such she abominated. Many a trick did she play upon these, some of which were painful to them in their consequences, and a good number of them have never been traced to this day. Of all the nuns, however, none other was regarded by her with so much detestation as St. Hypolite; for she was always believed to have betrayed St. Frances, and to have caused her murder. She was looked upon by us as the voluntary cause of her death, and of the crime which those of us committed, who, unwillingly, took part in her execution. We, on the contrary, being under the worst of fears for ourselves, in case of refusing to obey our masters and mistress, thought ourselves chargeable with less guilt, as unwilling assistants in a scene which it was impossible for us to prevent or delay. Jane has often spoken with me of the suspected informer, and always in terms of the greatest bitterness.

The Superior sometimes expressed commiseration for mad Jane Ray, but I never could tell whether she really believed her insane or not. I was always inclined to think, that she was willing to put up with some of her tricks, because they served to divert our minds from the painful and depressing circumstances in which we were placed. I knew the Superior's powers and habits of deception also, and that she would deceive us as willingly as anyone else.

Sometimes she proposed to send Jane to St. Anne's, a place near Quebec, celebrated for the pilgrimages made to it by persons differently afflicted. It is supposed that some peculiar virtue exists there, which will restore health to the sick; and I have heard stories told in corroboration of the common belief.

Many lame and blind persons, with others, visit St. Anne's every year, some of whom may be seen travelling on foot, and begging their food. The Superior would sometimes say that it was a pity that a woman like Jane Ray, capable of being so useful, should be unable to do her duties, in consequence of a malady which she thought might be cured by a visit to St. Anne's.

Yet to St. Anne's Jane was never sent, and her wild and various tricks continued as before. The rules of silence, which the others were so scrupulous in observing, she set at nought every hour; and as for other rules, she regarded them with as little respect when they stood in her way. She would now and then step out and stop the clock by which our exercises were regulated, and sometimes in this manner lengthened out our recreation till near twelve. At last the old nuns began to watch against such a trick, and would occasionally go out to see if the clock was going.

She once made a request that she might not eat with the other nuns, which was granted, as it seemed to proceed from a spirit of genuine humility, which made her regard herself as unworthy of our society.

It being most convenient, she was sent to the Superior's table, to take her meals after her; and it did not at first occur to the Superior that Jane, in this manner, profited by the change, by getting much better food than the rest of us. Thus there seemed to be always something deeper than anybody at first suspected, at the bottom of everything she did.

She was once directed to sweep a community-room, under the sleeping-chamber. This office had before been assigned to the other nuns, as a penance; but the Superior, considering that Jane Ray did little or nothing, determined thus to furnish her with some employment.

She declared to us that she would not sweep it long, as we might soon be assured. It happened that the stove by which the community-room was warmed in the winter, had its pipe carried through the floor of our sleeping-chamber, and thence across it in a direction opposite that in which the pipe of our stove was carried. It being then warm weather, the hole was left unstopped. After we had all retired to our beds, and while engaged in our silent prayers, we were suddenly alarmed by a bright blaze of fire, which burst from the hole in the floor, and threw sparks all around us. We thought the building was burning, and uttered cries of terror, regardless of the penances, the fear of which generally kept us silent.

The utmost confusion prevailed; for although we had solemnly vowed never to flee from the Convent even if it was on fire, we were extremely alarmed, and could not repress our feelings. We soon learnt the cause, for the flames ceased in a moment or two, and it was found that mad Jane Ray, after sweeping a little in the room beneath, had stuck a quantity of wet powder on the end of her broom, thrust it up through the hole in the ceiling into our apartment, and with a lighted paper set it on fire.

The date of this alarm I must refer to a time soon after that of the election riots; for I recollect that she found means to get possession of some of the powder which was prepared at that time for an emergency to which some thought the Convent was exposed.

She once asked for pen and paper, and then the Superior told her if she wrote to her friends she must see it. She replied that it was for no such purpose; she wanted to write her confession, and thus make it once for all. She wrote it, handed it to the priest, and he gave it to the Superior, who read it to us. It was full of offences which she had never committed, evidently written to throw ridicule on confession, and one of the most ludicrous productions I ever saw.

Our bedsteads were made with very narrow boards laid across them, on which the beds were laid. One day, while we were in the bed-chambers together, she proposed that we should misplace these boards. This was done, so that at night nearly a dozen nuns fell down upon the floor in getting into bed. A good deal of confusion naturally ensued, but the authors were not discovered. I was so conscience-stricken, however, that a week afterwards, while we were examining our consciences together, I told her I must confess the sin the next day. She replied, 'Do as you like, but you will be sorry for it.'

The next day, when we came before the Superior, I was just going to kneel and confess, when Jane, almost without giving me time to shut the door, threw herself at the Superior's feet and confessed the trick, and a penance was immediately laid upon me for the sin I had concealed.

There was an old nun who was a famous talker, whom we used to call La Mère (Mother). One night, Jane Ray got up, and secretly changed the caps of several of the nuns; and hers among the rest. In the morning there was great confusion, and such a scene as seldom occurred. She was severely blamed by La Mère, having been informed against by some of the nuns; and at last became so much enraged, that she attacked the old woman, and even took her by the throat. La Mère called on all present to come to her assistance, and several nuns interfered. Jane seized the opportunity afforded in the confusion, to beat some of her worst enemies quite severely, and afterward said, that she had intended to kill some of the rascally informers.

For a time Jane made us laugh so much at prayers, that the Superior forbade her going down with us at morning prayers; and she took the opportunity to sleep in the morning. When this was found out, she was forbidden to get into her bed again after leaving it, and then she would creep under it and take a nap on the floor. This she told us of one day, but threatened us if we ever betrayed her. At length she was missed at breakfast, as she would sometimes oversleep herself, and the Superior began to be more strict, and always inquired, in the morning, whether Jane Ray was in her place.

When the question was general none of us answered; but when it was addressed to some nun near her by name, as,

'Saint Eustace, is Jane Ray in her place?' then we had to reply.

Of all the scenes that occurred during my stay in the Convent, there was none which excited the delight of Jane more than one which took place in the chapel one day at mass, though I never had any particular reason to suppose that she had brought it about.

Some person unknown to me to this day, had put some substance or other, of a most nauseous smell, into the hat of a little boy, who attended at the altar, and he, without observing the trick, put it upon his head. In the midst of the ceremonies he approached some of the nuns, who were almost suffocated with the odour; and as he occasionally moved from place to place, some of them began to beckon to him to stand further off, and to hold their noses, with looks of disgust. The boy was quite unconscious of the cause of the difficulty, and paid them no attention, but the confusion soon became so great through the distress of some, and the laughing of others, that the Superior noticed the circumstance, and beckoned the boy to withdraw.

All attempts, however, to engage us in any work, prayer, or meditation, were found ineffectual. Whenever the circumstance in the chapel came to mind, we would laugh out. We had got into such a state, that we could not easily restrain ourselves. The Superior, yielding to necessity, allowed us recreation for the whole day.

The Superior used sometimes to send Jane to instruct the novices in their English prayers. She would proceed to the task with all seriousness; but sometimes chose the most ridiculous, as well as irreverent, passages from the songs, and other things, which she had sometimes learned, which would set us, who understood her, laughing. One of her rhymes, I recollect, began with—

> 'The Lord of love – look from above
> Upon this turkey hen!'

One winter's day, she was sent to light a fire; but after she had done so, remarked privately to some of us, 'my fingers were so cold – you'll see if I do it again.'

The next day there was a great stir in the house, because it was said that mad Jane Ray had been seized with a fit while making a fire, and she was taken up apparently insensible, and conveyed to her bed. She complained to me, who visited her in the course of the day, that she was likely to starve, as food was denied her; and I was persuaded to pin a stocking under my dress, and secretly put food into it from the table. This I afterwards carried to her, and relieved her wants.

One of the things which I had blamed Jane most for, was a disposition to quarrel with any nun who seemed to be winning the favour of the Superior. She would never rest until she had brought such a one into some difficulty.

Jane for a time slept opposite to me, and often in the night would rise, unobserved, and slip into my bed, to talk with me, which she did in a low whisper, and returned again with equal caution.

She would tell me of the tricks she had played, and such as she meditated, and sometimes make me laugh so loud, that I had much to do in the morning with begging pardons and doing penances.

We were allowed but little soap; and Jane, when she found her supply nearly gone, would take the first piece she could find. One day there was a general search made for a large piece that was missed; when, soon after I had been searched, Jane Ray passed me, and slipped it into my pocket; she soon after was searched herself, and then secretly came for it again.

While I recall these particulars of our Nunnery, and refer so often to the conduct and language of one of the nuns, I cannot speak of some things, which I believed or suspected, on account of my want of sufficient knowledge. But it is a pity you have not Jane Ray for a witness; she knew many things of which I am ignorant. She must be in possession of facts that should be known. Her long residence in the Convent, her habits of roaming about it, and of observing everything, must have made her acquainted with things which would be heard with interest. I always felt as if she knew everything. She would often go and listen, or look through the cracks into the Superior's room, while any of the priests were closeted with her and sometimes would come and tell me what she witnessed. I felt myself bound to confess on such occasions, and always did so.

She knew, however, that I only told it to the priest, or to the Superior, and without mentioning the name of my informant, which I was at liberty to withhold, so that she was not found out. I often said to her, 'Don't tell me, Jane, for I must confess it.' She would reply, 'It is better for you to confess it than for me.' I thus became, even against my will, informed of scenes supposed by the actors of them to be secret.

Jane Ray once persuaded me to accompany her into the Superior's room, to hide with her under the sofa, and await the appearance of a visitor whom she expected, that we might overhear what passed between them. We had been long concealed, when the Superior came in alone, and sat for some time; when, fearing she might detect us in the stillness that prevailed, we began to repent of our temerity. At length, however, she suddenly withdrew, and thus afforded us a welcome opportunity to escape.

I was passing one day through a part of the cellar, where I had not often occasion to go, when the toe of my shoe hit something. I tripped and fell down. I rose again, and holding my lamp to see what had caused my fall, I found an iron ring, fastened to a small square trap-door. This I had the curiosity to raise, and saw four or five steps down, but there was not light enough to see more, and I feared to be noticed by somebody and reported to the Superior; so, closing the door again, I left the spot. At first I could not imagine the use of such a passage; but it afterwards occurred to me that it might open to the subterranean passage to the Seminary; for I never could before account for the appearance of many of the priests, who often appeared and disappeared among us, particularly at night, when I knew the gates were closed. They could, as I now saw, come up to the door of the Superior's room at any hour; then up the stairs into our sleeping-room, or where they chose. And often they were in our beds before us.

I afterwards ascertained that my conjectures were correct, and that a secret communication was kept up in this manner between these two institutions, at the end towards Nôtre Dame street, at a considerable depth under ground. I often afterwards met priests in the cellar, when sent there for coals and other articles, as they had to pass up and down the common cellar stairs on their way.

My wearisome daily prayers and labours, my pain of **body**

and depression of mind, which were so much increased by
penances I had suffered, and those which I constantly
reared, and the feelings of shame, remorse, and horror,
which sometimes arose, brought me to a state which I
cannot describe.

In the first place, my frame was enfeebled by the uneasy
postures I was required to keep for so long a time during
prayers. This alone, I thought, was sufficient to undermine
my health and destroy my life. An hour and a half every
morning I had to sit on the floor of the community-room,
with my feet under me, my body bent forward, and my
head hanging on one side, in a posture expressive of great
humility, it is true, but very fatiguing to keep for such an un-
reasonable length of time. Often I found it impossible to
avoid falling asleep in this posture, which I could do without detection, by bending a little lower than usual. The
signal to rise, or the noise made by the rising of the other
nuns, then woke me, and I got up with the rest unobserved.

Before we took the posture just described, we had to kneel
for a long time without bending the body, keeping quite
erect with the exception of the knees only, with the hands
together before the breast. This I found the most distressing attitude for me, and never assumed it without feeling
a sharp pain in my chest, which I often thought would soon
lead me to my grave – that is, to the great common
receptacle for the dead under the chapel. And this upright
kneeling posture we were obliged to resume as soon as we
rose from the half-sitting posture first mentioned, so that I
usually felt myself exhausted and near to fainting before
the conclusion of morning services.

I found the meditations extremely tedious, and often did
I sink into sleep, while we were all seated in silence on the
floor. When required to tell my meditations, as it was
thought to be of no great importance what we said, I sometimes found that I had nothing to tell but a dream, and told
that, which passed off very well.

Jane Ray appeared to be troubled still more than myself

with wandering thoughts; and when blamed for them, would reply, 'I begin very well; but directly I begin to think of some old friend of mine, and my thoughts go a-wandering from one country to another.'

Sometimes I confessed my falling asleep; and often the priests have talked to me about the sin of sleeping in the time of meditation. At last, one of them proposed to me that I should prick myself with a pin, which is often done, and so rouse myself for a time.

My close confinement in the Convent, and the want of opportunities to breathe the open air, might have proved more injurious to me than they did, had I not employed a part of my time in more active labours than those of sewing &c., to which I was chiefly confined. I took part occasionally in some of the heavy work, as washing, &c.

The events which I am now to relate occurred about five months after my admission into the Convent as a nun; but I cannot fix the time with precision, as I know not of anything that took place in the world about the same period. The circumstance I clearly remember; but as I have elsewhere remarked, we were not accustomed to keep any account of time.

Information was given to us one day, that another novice was to be admitted among us; and we were required to remember and mention her often in our prayers, that she might have faithfulness in the service of her holy spouse. No information was given us concerning her beyond this fact; not a word about her age, name, or nation. On all similar occasions the same course was pursued, and all that the nuns ever learnt concerning one another was what they might discover by being together, and which usually amounted to little or nothing.

When the day of her admission arrived, though I did not witness the ceremony in the chapel, it was a gratification to us all on one account, because we were always released from labour, and enjoyed a great recreation day.

Our new sister, when she was introduced to the 'holy'

society of us 'saints,' proved to be young, of about the middle size, and very good-looking for a Canadian; for I soon ascertained that she was one of my own countrywomen. The Canadian females are generally not handsome. I never learnt her name nor anything of her history. She had chosen St. Martin for her nun name. She was admitted in the morning, and appeared melancholy all day. This I observed was always the case; and the remarks made by others, led me to believe that they, and all they had seen, had felt sad and miserable for a longer or shorter time. Even the Superior, as it may be recollected, confessed to me that she experienced the same feelings when she was received. When bed-time arrived, she proceeded to the chamber with the rest of us, and was assigned a bed on the side of the room opposite my own, and a little beyond. The nuns were all soon in bed, the usual silence ensued, and I was making my customary mental prayers, and composing myself to sleep, when I heard the most piercing and heart-rending shrieks proceed from our new comrade. Every nun seemed to rise as if by one impulse, for no one could hear such sounds, especially in such total silence, without being greatly excited. A general noise succeeded, for many voices spoke together, uttering cries of surprise, compassion, or fear. It was in vain for the night-watch to expect silence: for once we forgot rules and penances, and gave vent to our feelings, she could do nothing but call for the Superior.

I heard a man's voice mingled with the cries and shrieks of the nun. Father Quiblier, of the Seminary, I had felt confident, was in the Superior's room at the time when we retired; and several of the nuns afterwards assured me that it was he. The Superior soon made her appearance, and in a harsh manner commanded silence. I heard her threaten gagging her, and then say, 'You are no better than anybody else, and if you do not obey, you shall be sent to the cells.'

One young girl was taken into the Convent during my abode there, under peculiar circumstances. I was acquainted with the whole affair, as I was employed to act a part in it.

Among the novices was a young lady, of about seventeen, the daughter of an old rich Canadian. She had been remarkable for nothing that I know of, except the liveliness of her disposition. The Superior once expressed to us a wish to have her take the veil, though the girl herself had never such intention that I know of. Why the Superior wished to receive her I could only conjecture. One reason might have been, that she expected to receive a considerable sum from her father. She was, however, strongly desirous of having the girl in our community, and one day said – 'Let us take her in by a trick, and tell the old man she felt too humble to take the veil in public.'

In obedience to the directions of the Superior we exerted ourselves to make her contented, especially when she was first received, when we got round her and told her we had felt so for a time, but having since become acquainted with the happiness of a nun's life, were perfectly content, and would never be willing to leave the Convent. An exception seemed to be made in her favour, in one respect; for I believe no criminal attempt was made upon her, until she had been for some time an inmate of the nunnery.

Soon after her reception, or rather her forcible entry into the Convent, her father called to make inquiries about his daughter. The Superior spoke first with him herself, and then called us to repeat her plausible story, which I did with accuracy. If I had wished to say anything else, I never should have dared.

We told the foolish old man, that his daughter, whom we all affectionately loved, had long desired to become a nun, but had been too humble to wish to appear before spectators, and had, at her own desire, been favoured with a private admission into the community.

The benefit conferred upon himself and his family, by this act of self-consecration, I reminded him, must be truly great and valuable; as every family who furnishes a priest or a nun, is justly looked upon as receiving the peculiar favour of heaven on that account. The old Canadian, firmly believing every word I was forced to tell him, took the event as a great blessing, and expressed the greatest readiness to pay more than the customary fee to the Convent.

After the interview, he withdrew, promising soon to return, and pay a handsome sum of money to the Convent, which he performed with all despatch and the greatest cheerfulness. The poor girl never heard that her father had taken the trouble to call and see her, much less did she know anything of the imposition passed upon her. She remained in the Convent when I left it.

The youngest girl who ever took the veil of our sisterhood, was only fourteen years of age, and considered very pious. She lived but a short time. I was told that she was ill-treated by the priests, and believed her death was in consequence.

CHAPTER XIV

It was considered a great duty to exert ourselves to influence novices in favour of the Roman Catholic religion; and different nuns were, at different times, charged to do what they could, by conversation, to make favourable impressions on the minds of some, who were particularly indicated to us by the Superior. I often heard it remarked, that those who were influenced with the greatest difficulty, were young ladies from the United States; and on some of those great exertions were made.

Cases in which citizens of the States were said to have been converted to the Roman Catholic faith were sometimes spoken of, and always as if they were considered highly important.

The Bishop, as we were told, was in the public square, on the day of an execution, when, as he said a stranger looked at him in some peculiar manner, which made him confidently believe God intended to have him converted by his means. When he went home he wrote a letter for him, and the next day he found him again in the same place, and gave him the letter, which led to his becoming a Roman Catholic. This man, it was added, proved to be a citizen of the States.

The Bishop, as I have remarked, was not very dignified on all occasions, and sometimes acted in such a manner as would not have appeared well in public.

One day I saw him preparing for mass; and because he had some difficulty in getting on his robes, showed evident signs of anger. One of the nuns remarked: 'The Bishop is going to perform a passionate mass.' Some of the others exclaimed: 'Are you not ashamed to speak thus of my lord?' And she was rewarded with a penance.

But it might be hoped that the Bishop would be free from the crimes of which I have declared so many priests to have been guilty. I am far from entertaining such charitable opinions of him; and I had good reasons, after a time.

I was often required to sleep on a sofa, in the room of the present Superior, as I may have already mentioned.

One night, not long after I was first introduced there for that purpose, and within the first twelve months of my wearing the veil, having retired as usual, at about half past nine, not long after we had got into bed, the alarm-bell from without, which hangs over the Superior's bed, was rung. She told me to see who was there; and going down, I heard the signal given, which I have before mentioned, a peculiar kind of hissing sound made through the teeth. I answered with a low 'Hum – hum;' and then opened the door. It was Bishop Lartique, the present Bishop of Montreal. He said to me, 'Are you a Novice or a Received?' meaning a Received nun. I answered, 'a Received.'

He then requested me to conduct him to the Superior's room, which I did. He went to the bed, drew the curtains behind him, and I lay down again upon the sofa, until morning, when the Superior called me, at an early hour, about daylight, and directed me to show him the door, to which I conducted him, and he took his departure.

I continued to visit the cellar frequently, to carry up coal for the fires, without anything more than a general impression that there were two nuns somewhere imprisoned in it. One day, while there on my usual errand, I saw a nun standing on the right of the cellar, in front of one of the cell doors I had before observed; she was apparently engaged with something within. This attracted my attention. The door appeared to close in a small recess, and was fastened with a stout iron bolt on the outside, the end of which was secured by being let into a hole in the stonework which formed the posts. The door, which was of wood, was sunk a few inches beyond the stonework, which rose and formed an arch overhead. Above the bolt was a small window, supplied with a fine grating, which swung open, a small bolt having been removed from it, on the outside. The nun I had observed seemed to be whispering with some person within, through the little window; but I hastened to get my coal, and left the cellar, presuming that was the prison. When I visited the place again, being alone, I ventured to the spot, determined to learn the truth, presuming that the imprisoned nuns, of whom the Superior had told me on my admission, were confined there. I spoke at the window where I had seen the nun standing, and heard a voice reply in a whisper. The aperture was so small, and the place so dark, that I could see nobody; but I learnt that a poor wretch was confined there a prisoner. I feared that I might be discovered, and after a few words, which I thought could do no harm, I withdrew.

My curiosity was now alive to learn everything I could about so mysterious a subject. I made a few inquiries of St. Xavier, who only informed me that they were punished for refusing to obey the Superior, Bishop, and Priests. I afterwards found that the other nuns were acquainted with the fact I had just discovered. All I could learn, however, was that the prisoner in the cell whom I had just spoken with, and another in the cell just beyond, had been confined there several years without having been taken out; but their

names, connexions, offences, and everything else relating
to them, I could never learn, and am still as ignorant of as
ever. Some conjectured that they had refused to comply
with some of the rules of the Convent, or requisitions of the
Superior; others, that they were heiresses whose property
was desired for the Convent, and who would not consent to
sign deeds of it. Some of the nuns informed me, that the
severest of their sufferings arose from fear of supernatural
beings.

I often spoke with one of them in passing near their cells,
when on errands in the cellar, but never ventured to stop
long, or to press my inquiries very far. Besides, I found her
reserved, and little disposed to converse freely, a thing I
could not wonder at when I considered her situation, and
the character of persons around her. She spoke like a woman
in feeble health, and of broken spirits. I occasionally saw
other nuns speaking to them, particularly at meal times,
when they were regularly furnished with food, which was
such as we ourselves ate.

Their cells were occasionally cleaned, and then the doors
were opened. I never looked into them, but was informed
that the ground was their only floor. I presumed that they
were furnished with straw to lie upon, as I always saw a
quantity of old straw scattered about that part of the
cellar, after the cells had been cleaned. I once inquired of
one of them whether they could converse together, and she
replied that they could, through a small opening between
their cells, which I could not see.

I once inquired of the one I spoke with in passing,
whether she wanted anything, and she replied, 'Tell Jane
Ray I want to see her a moment if she can slip away.' When
I went up I took an opportunity to deliver my message to
Jane, who concerted with me a signal to be used in future,
in case a similar request should be made through me. This
was a sly wink at her with one eye, accompanied with a
slight toss of the head. She then sought an opportunity to
visit the cellar, and was soon able to hold an interview with

the poor prisoners, without being noticed by anyone but myself. I afterwards learnt that mad Jane Ray was not so mad but she could feel for those miserable beings, and carry through measures for their comfort. She would often visit them with sympathizing words, and when necessary, conceal part of her food while at table, and secretly convey it into their dungeons. Sometimes we would combine for such an object; and have repeatedly aided her in thus obtaining a larger supply of food than they had been able to obtain from others.

I frequently thought of the two nuns confined in the cells, and occasionally heard something said about them, but very little. Whenever I visited the cellar and thought it safe, I went up to the first of them and spoke a word or two, and usually got some brief reply, without ascertaining that any particular change took place with either of them. The one with whom alone I ever conversed, spoke English perfectly well, and French I thought as well. I supposed she must have been well educated, for I could not tell which was her native language. I remember that she frequently used these words when I wished to say more to her, and which alone showed that she was constantly afraid of punishment, 'Oh, there's somebody coming – do go away!' I have been told that the other prisoner also spoke English.

It was impossible for me to form any certain opinion about the size or appearance of those two miserable creatures, for their cells were perfectly dark, and I never caught the slightest glimpse even of their faces. It is probable they were women not above the middle size, and my reason for this presumption is the following: I was sometimes appointed to lay out the clean clothes for all the nuns in the Convent on Saturday evening, and was always directed to lay by two suits for the prisoners. Particular orders were given to select the largest sized garments for several tall nuns; but nothing of the kind was ever said in relation to the clothes for those in the cells.

I had not been long a veiled nun, before I requested of the

Superior permission to confess to the 'Saint Bon Pasteur,' (Holy Good Shepherd) that is, the mysterious and nameless nun whom I had heard of while a novice. I knew of several others who had confessed to her at different times, and of some who had sent their clothes to be touched by her when they were sick; and I felt a desire to unburden my heart of certain things, which I was loath to acknowledge to the Superior, or any of the priests.

The Superior made me wait a little, until she could ascertain whether the 'Saint Bon Pasteur' was ready to admit me; and, after a time, returned, and told me to enter the old nuns' room. That apartment has twelve beds arranged like the berths of a ship, by threes; and as each is broad enough to receive two persons, twenty-four may be lodged there, which was about the number of old nuns in the Convent during most of my stay in it. Near an opposite corner of the apartment was a large glass case, with no appearance of a door, or other opening, in any part of it; and in that case stood the venerable nun, in the dress of the community, with her thick veil spread over her face, so as to conceal it entirely. She was standing, for the place did not allow room for sitting, and moved a little, which was the only sign of life, as she did not speak. I fell upon my knees before her, and began to confess some of my imperfections, that I might be delivered from them. She appeared to listen to me with patience, but still never returned a word in reply. I became much affected as I went on; at length began to weep bitterly: and, when I withdrew, was in tears. It seemed to me that my heart was remarkably relieved, after this exercise; and all the requests I had made, I found, as I believed, strictly fulfilled. I often, afterwards, visited the old nuns' room for the same purpose, and with similar results; so that my belief in the sanctity of the nameless nun, and my regard for her intercession, were unbounded.

What is remarkable, though I repeatedly was sent into that room to dust it, or to put it in order, I remarked, that the glass case was vacant, and no signs were to be found, either of the nun, or of the way by which she had left it! so that a solemn conclusion rested upon my mind, that she had gone on one of her frequent visits to heaven.

A priest would sometimes come in the daytime to teach us to sing, and this was done with some parade or stir, as if it were considered, or meant to be considered, as a thing of importance.

The instructions, however, were entirely repetitions of the words and tunes, nothing being taught even of the first principles of the science. It appeared to me that although hymns alone were sung, the exercise was chiefly designed for our amusement, to raise our spirits a little, which were apt to become depressed. Mad Jane Ray certainly usually treated the whole thing as a matter of sport, and often excited those of us who understood English, to a great degree of mirth. She had a very fine voice, which was so powerful as generally to be heard above the rest. Sometimes she would be silent when the other nuns began; and the Superior would often call out, 'Jane Ray, you don't sing.' She always had some trifling excuse ready, and commonly appeared unwilling to join the rest.

After being urged or commanded by the Superior, she would then strike up some English song, or profane parody, which was rendered ten times more ridiculous by the ignorance of the lady Superior and the majority of the nuns. I cannot help laughing now when I remember how she used to stand with perfect composure, and sing,

> 'I wish I was married and nothing to rue,
> With plenty of money and nothing to do.'

'Jane Ray, you don't sing right,' the Superior would exclaim. 'Oh,' she would reply with perfect coolness, 'that is the English for

> 'Seigneur Dieu de clémence,
> Reçois ce grand pécheur!'

and, as sung by her, a person ignorant of the language

would naturally be imposed upon. It was extremely difficult for me to conceal my laughter. I have always had
greater exertion to make in repressing it than most other
persons; and mad Jane Ray often took advantage of this.

Saturday evening usually brought with it much unpleasant work for some of us. We received Sacrament every
Sunday; and in preparation for it, on Saturday evening, we
asked pardon of the Superior, and of each other, 'for the
scandal we had caused them since we last received the
Sacrament', and then asked the Superior's permission to
receive it on the following day. She inquired of each nun,
who necessarily asked her permission, whether she, naming
her as Saint somebody, had concealed any sin that should
hinder her receiving it; and if the answer was in the nega-
tive, she granted her permission.

On Saturday we were catechized by a priest, being
assembled in a community-room. He sat on the right of the
door, in a chair. He often told us stories, and frequently
enlarged on the duty of enticing novices into the nunnery.
'Do you not feel happy,' he would say, 'now that you are
safely out of the world, and sure of heaven? But remember
how many poor people are yet in the world. Every novice
you influence to take the black veil, will add to your honour
in heaven. Tell them how happy you are.'

The Superior played one trick while I was in the Convent,
which always passed for one of the most admirable she ever
carried into execution. We were pretty good judges in a case
of this kind; for, as may be presumed, we were rendered
familiar with the arts of deception under so accomplished
a teacher.

There was an ornament on hand in the Nunnery, of an
extraordinary kind, which was prized at ten pounds; but
it had been exposed to view so long, that it became damaged
and quite unsaleable. We were one day visited by an old
priest from the country, who was evidently somewhat in-
toxicated; and as he withdrew to go to his lodgings in the
Seminary, where the country priests often stay, the Superior

conceived a plan for disposing of the old ornament. 'Come,' said she, 'we will send it to the old priest, and swear he has bought it.'

We all approved of the ingenious device, for it evidently classed among the pious frauds we had so often had recommended to us, both by precept and example; and the ornament was sent to him the next morning, as his property when paid for. He soon came into the Convent, and expressed the greatest surprise that he had been charged with purchasing such a thing, for which he had no need and no desire.

The Superior heard his declaration with patience, but politely insisted that it was a fair bargain; and we then surrounded the old priest, with the strongest assertions that such was the fact, and that nobody would have thought of his purchasing it unless he had expressly engaged to take it. The poor old man was entirely put down. He was certain of the truth; but what could he do to resist or disprove a direct falsehood pronounced by the Superior of a Convent, and sworn to by all her holy nuns? He finally expressed his conviction that we were right: and was compelled to pay his money.

CHAPTER XV

SOME of the priests from the Seminary were in the Nunnery every day and night, and often several at a time. I have seen nearly all of them at different times, though there are about one hundred and fifty in the district of Montreal. There was a difference in their conduct: though I believe every one of them was guilty of licentiousness; while not one did I ever see who maintained a character any way becoming the profession of a priest. Some were gross and degraded in a degree which few of my readers can ever have imagined: and I should be unwilling to offend the eye, and corrupt the heart, of anyone by an account of their words and actions. Few imaginations can conceive deeds so abominable as they practised, and often required of some of the poor women, under the fear of severe punishments, and even of death. I do not hesitate to say with the strongest confidence, that although some of the nuns became lost to every sentiment of virtue and honour, especially one of the Congregational Nunnery whom I have before mentioned, Saint Patrick, the greater part of them loathed the practices to which they were compelled to submit, by their Superior and priests, who kept them under so dreadful a bondage.

Some of the priests whom I saw I never knew by name, and the names of the others I did not learn for a time, and at last learnt only by accident.

They were always called 'Mon Père,' (my father), but sometimes when they had purchased something in the ornament-room, they would give their real names, with directions where it should be sent. Many names thus learnt, and in other ways, were whispered about from nun to nun, and became pretty generally known. Several of the priests some of us had seen before we entered the Convent.

Many things of which I speak, from the nature of the case, must necessarily rest chiefly upon my own word, until further evidence can be obtained; but there are some facts for which I can appeal to the knowledge of others. It is commonly known in Montreal that some of the priests occasionally withdraw from their customary employments, and are not to be seen for some time; it being understood that they have retired for religious study, meditation, and devotion, for the improvement of their hearts. Sometimes they are thus withdrawn from the world for three weeks: but there is no fixed period.

This was a fact I knew before I took the veil; for it is a frequent subject of remark, that such and such a Father is on a 'holy retreat.' This is a term which conveys the idea of a religious seclusion from the world, for sacred purposes.

On the reappearance of a priest after such a period, in the church or the streets, it is natural to feel a peculiar impression of his devout character – an impression very different from that conveyed to the mind who knows matters as they really are. Suspicions have been indulged by some in Canada on this subject, and facts are known by at least a few. I am able to speak from personal knowledge; for I have been a nun of Soeur Bourgeoise.

The priests are liable, by their dissolute habits, to occasional attacks of disease, which render it necessary, or at least prudent, to submit to medical treatment.

In the Black Nunnery they find private accommodation, for they are free to enter one of the private hospitals whenever they please; which is a room set apart on purpose for the accommodation of the priests, and is called a retreat-room. But an excuse is necessary to blind the public, and this they find in the pretence they make of being in a 'Holy Retreat.' Many such cases have I known; and I can mention the names of priests who have been confined in this Holy Retreat. They are very carefully attended by the Superior and old nuns, and their diet consists mostly of vegetable soups, &c., with but little meat, and that fresh. I have seen an instrument of surgery lying upon the table in that holy room, which is used only for particular purposes.

Father Tombeau, a Roman priest, was on one of his holy retreats about the time when I left the Nunnery. There are sometimes a number confined there at the same time. The victims of these priests frequently share the same fate.

I have often reflected how grievously I had been deceived in my opinions of a nun's condition!—All the holiness of their lives, I now saw was merely pretended. The appearance of sanctity and heavenly-mindedness which they had shown among us novices, I found was only a disguise to conceal such practices as would not be tolerated in any decent society in the world; and as for joy and peace like that of heaven, which I had expected to find among them, I learnt too well that they did not exist there.

The only way in which such thoughts were counteracted, was by the constant instructions given us by the Superior and priests, to regard every doubt as a mortal sin. Other faults we might have, as we were told over and over again, which, though worthy of penances, were far less sinful than these. For a nun to doubt that she was doing her duty in fulfilling her vows and oaths, was a heinous of-fence, and we were exhorted always to suppress our doubts, to confess them without reserve, and cheerfully submit to severe penances on account of them, as the only means of mortifying our evil dispositions, and resisting the tempta-tions of the devil. Thus we learnt in a good degree to re-sist our minds and consciences, when we felt the rising of a question about the duty of doing anything required of us.

To enforce this upon us they employed various means. Some of the most striking stories told us at catechism by the priests, were designed for this end. One of these I will repeat. 'One day,' as a priest assured us, who was hear-ing us say the catechism on Saturday afternoon, 'as one Monsieur * * * *, a well-known citizen of Montreal, was walking near the cathedral, he saw Satan giving orders to innumerable evil spirits who were assembled around him. Being afraid of being seen, and yet wishing to observe what was done, he hid himself where he could observe all that passed. Satan despatched his devils to different parts of the city, with directions to do their best for him; and returned in a short time, bringing in reports of their suc-cess in leading persons of different classes to the commis-sion of various sins, which they thought would be agree-able to their master. Satan, however, expressed his dissatis-faction, and ordered them out again; but just then a spirit from the Black Nunnery came, who had not been seen before, and stated that he had been trying for seven years to persuade one of the nuns to doubt, and had just succeeded. Satan received the intelligence with the highest pleasure; and turning to the spirits around him, said: 'You have not half done your work, – he has done much more than all of you put together.'

In spite, however, of our instructions and warnings, our fears and penances, such doubts would obtrude; and I have often indulged them for a time, and at length, yielding to the belief that I was wrong in giving place to them, would confess them, and undergo with cheerfulness such new penances as I was loaded with. Others too would occasionally entertain and privately express such doubts; though we had all been most solemnly warned by the cruel murder of Saint Frances. Occasionally some of the nuns would go further, and resist the restraints of punishments imposed upon them; and it was not uncommon to hear screams, sometimes of a most piercing and terrific kind, from nuns suffering under discipline.

Some of my readers may feel disposed to exclaim against me, for believing things which will strike them as so monstrous and abominable. To such, I would say, without pretending to justify myself, – you know little of the position in which I was placed; to begin with, ignorant of any other religious doctrines, and secondly, met at every moment by some ingenious argument, and the example of a large community, who received all the instructions of the priests as of undoubted truth, and practised upon them. Of the variety and speciousness of the arguments used, you cannot have any correct idea. They were often so ready with replies, examples, anecdotes, and authorities, to enforce their doctrines, that it seemed to me as if they could never have learnt it all from books, but must have been taught by wicked spirits. Indeed, when I reflect upon their conversations, I am astonished at their art and address, and find it difficult to account for their subtlety and success in influencing my mind, and persuading me to anything they pleased. It seems to me that hardly anybody would be safe in their hands. If you were to go to confession twice, I believe you would feel very different from what you do now. They have such a way of avoiding one thing and speaking of another, of affirming this, and doubting and disputing that, of quoting authorities, and speaking of wonders and miracles recently performed, in confirmation of what they teach, as familiarly known to persons whom they call by name, and whom they pretend to offer as witnesses, though they never give you an opportunity to speak with them – these, and many other means, they use in such a way, that they always blinded my mind, and, I should think, would blind the minds of others.

CHAPTER XVI

It will be recollected, that I was informed immediately after receiving the veil, that infants were occasionally murdered in the Convent. I was one day in the nuns' private sick-room, when I had an opportunity, unsought for, of witnessing deeds of such nature. It was, perhaps, a month after the death of St. Frances. Two little twin babes, the children of St. Catherine, were brought to a priest, who was in the room for baptism. I was present while the ceremony was performed, with the Superior and several of the old nuns, whose names I never knew, they being called Ma tante (Aunt).

The priests took turns in attending to confession and catechism in the Convent, usually three months at a time, though sometimes longer periods. The priest then on duty was Father Larkin. He is a good-looking European, and has a brother who is a Professor in the College. He first put oil upon the heads of the infants, as is the custom before baptism. When he had baptized the children, they were taken, one after another, by one of the old nuns, in the presence of us all. She pressed her hand upon the mouth and nose of the first so tight that it could not breathe, and in a few minutes, when the hand was removed, it was dead. She then took the other, and treated it in the same way. No sound was heard, and both the children were corpses. The greatest indifference was shown by all present during this operation, for all, as I well knew, were long accustomed to such scenes. The little bodies were then taken into the cellar, thrown into the pit I have mentioned, and covered with a quantity of lime.

I afterwards saw a new-born infant treated in the same manner, in the same place; but the actors in this scene I choose not to name, nor the circumstances, as everything connected with it is of a peculiarly trying and painful nature to my own feelings.

These were the only instances of infanticide I witnessed; and it seemed to be merely owing to accident that I was then present. So far as I know there were no pains taken to preserve secrecy on this subject; that is, I saw no attempt made to keep any inmate of the Convent in ignorance of the murder of the children. On the contrary, others were told, as well as myself, on their first admission as veiled nuns, that all infants born in the place were baptized and killed, without loss of time; and I had been called to witness the murder of the three just mentioned, only because I happened to be in the room at the time.

That others were killed in the same manner, during my stay in the nunnery, I am well assured.

How many there were I cannot tell, and having taken no account of those I heard of, I cannot speak with precision; I believe, however, what I learn through nuns, that at least eighteen or twenty infants were smothered, and secretly buried in the cellar, while I was a nun.

One of the effects of the weariness of our bodies and minds, was our proneness to talk in our sleep. It was both ludicrous and painful to hear the nuns repeat their prayers in the course of the night, as they frequently did in their dreams. Required to keep our minds continually on the stretch, in watching our conduct, in remembering the rules and our prayers, under the fear of the consequences of any neglect, when we closed our eyes in sleep, we often went over again the scenes of the day, and it was no uncommon thing for me to hear a nun repeat one or two of her long exercises in the dead of the night. Sometimes by the time she had finished, another, in a different part of the room, would happen to take a similar turn, and commence a similar recitation; and I have known cases in which several such unconscious exercises were performed, all within an hour or two.

We had now and then a recreation day, when we were relieved from our customary labour, and from all prayers except those for morning and evening, and the short ones said at every striking of the clock. The greater part of our time was then occupied with different games, particularly backgammon and draughts, and in such conversation as did not relate to our past lives, and the outside of the Convent. Sometimes, however, our sports would be interrupted on such days by the entrance of one of the priests, who would come in and propose that his fête, the birthday of his patron saint, should be kept by 'the saints.' We saints!

Several nuns died at different times while I was in the Convent; how many, I cannot say, but there was a considerable number. I might rather say many in proportion to the number in the nunnery. The proportion of deaths I am sure was very large. There were always some in the nuns' sick-room, and several interments took place in the chapel.

When a Black Nun is dead, the corpse is dressed as if living, and placed in the chapel in a sitting posture, within the railing round the altar, with a book in hand as if reading. Persons are then freely admitted from the street, and some of them read and pray before it. No particular notoriety is given, I believe, to this exhibition out of the Convent, but such a case usually excites some attention.

The living nuns are required to say prayers for the delivery of their deceased sister from purgatory, being informed, as in all other such cases, that if she is not there, and has no need of our intercession, our prayers are in no danger of being thrown away, as they will be set down to the account of some of our deceased friends, or at least to that of the souls which have no acquaintances to pray for them.

It was customary for us occasionally to kneel before a dead nun thus seated in the chapel, and I have often performed that task. It was always painful, for the ghastly countenance being seen whenever I raised my eyes, and the feeling that the position and dress were entirely opposed to every idea of propriety in such a case, always made me melancholy.

The Superior sometimes left the Convent, and was absent for an hour, or several hours at a time, but we never knew of it until she had returned, and were not informed where she had been. I one day had reason to presume that she had recently paid a visit to the priests' farm, though I had not direct evidence that such was the fact. The priests' farm is a fine tract of land belonging to the Seminary, a little distance from the city, near the Lachine road, with a large old-fashioned edifice upon it. I happened to be in the Superior's room on the day alluded to, when she made some remarks on the plainness and poverty of her furniture. I replied that she was not proud, and could not be dissatisfied on that account; she answered, – 'No; but if I was, how much superior is the furniture at the priests' farm; the poorest room there is furnished better than the best of mine.'

I was one day mending the fire in the Superior's room, when a priest was conversing with her on the scarcity of money; and I heard him say that very little money was received by the priests for prayers, but that the principal part came with penances and absolutions.

One of the most remarkable and unaccountable things that happened in the Convent, was the disappearance of the old Superior. She had performed her customary part during the day, and had acted and appeared just as usual. She had shown no symptoms of ill health, met with no particular difficulty in conducting business, and no agitation, anxiety, or gloom had been noticed in her conduct. We had no reason to suppose that during that day she had expected anything particular to occur, any more than the rest of us. After the close of our customary labours and evening lectures, she dismissed us to retire to bed, exactly in her usual manner. The next morning the bell rang, we sprang from our beds, hurried on our clothes, as usual, and proceeded to the community-room in double line, to commence the morning exercises. There, to our surprise, we found Bishop Lartique; but the Superior was nowhere to be seen. The Bishop soon addressed us, instead of her, and informed us, that a lady near him, whom he presented to us, was now the Superior of the Convent, and enjoined upon us the same respect and obedience which we paid to her predecessor.

The lady he introduced to us was one of our oldest nuns, Saint Du, a very large, fleshy woman, with swelled limbs, which rendered her very slow in walking, and often gave her great distress. Not a word was dropped from which we could conjecture the cause of this change, nor of the fate of the old Superior. I took the first opportunity to inquire of one of the nuns, whom I dared to talk to, what had become of her; but I found them as ignorant as myself, though suspicious that she had been murdered by order of the Bishop. Never did I obtain any light on her mysterious disappearance. I am confident, however, that if the Bishop wished to get rid of her privately, and by foul means, he had ample opportunities and power at his command. Jane Ray, as usual, could not allow such an occurrence to pass by without intimating her own suspicions more plainly than any other of the nuns would have dared to. She spoke out one day in the community-room, and said, 'I'm going to have a hunt in the cellar for my old Superior.'

'Hush, Jane Ray!' exclaimed some of the nuns, 'you'll be punished.'

'My mother used to tell me,' replied Jane, 'never to be afraid of the face of man.'

It cannot be thought strange that we were superstitious.

Some were more easily terrified than others by unaccountable sights and sounds; but all of us believed in the power and occasional appearance of spirits, and were ready to look for them at almost any time. I have seen several instances of alarm caused by such superstition, and have experienced it myself more than once. I was one day sitting mending aprons, beside one of the old nuns, in the community-room, while the litanies were repeating: as I was very easy to laugh, Saint Ignace, or Agnes, came in, walked up to her with much agitation, and began to whisper in her ear. She usually talked but little, and that made me more curious to know what was the matter. I overheard her say to the old nun, in much alarm, that in the cellar from which she had just returned, she had heard the most dreadful groans that ever came from any human being. This was enough to give me uneasiness. I could not account for the appearance of an evil spirit in any part of the Convent, for I had been assured that the only one ever known there was that of the nun who had died with an unconfessed sin; and that others were kept at a distance by the holy water that was rather profusely used in different parts of the nunnery. Still, I presumed that the sounds heard by Saint Ignace must have proceeded from some devil, and I felt great dread at the thought of visiting the cellar again. I determined to seek further information of the terrified nun, but when I addressed her on the subject, at recreation-time, the first opportunity I could find, she replied, that I was always trying to break her silence, and walked off to another group in the room, so that I could obtain no satisfaction.

It is remarkable that in our nunnery, we were almost entirely cut off from the means of knowing anything even of each other. There were many nuns whom I know nothing of to this day, after having been in the same rooms with them every day and night for four years. There was a nun, whom I supposed to be in the Convent, and whom I was anxious to learn something about from the time of my entrance as a novice; but I never was able to learn anything concerning her, not even whether she was in the nunnery or not, whether alive or dead. She was the daugher of a rich family, residing at Point aux Trembles, of whom I had heard my mother speak before I entered the Convent. The name of her family I think was Lafayette, and she was thought to be from Europe. She was known to have taken the Black Veil; but as I was not acquainted with the Saint she had assumed, and I could not describe her in 'the world', all my inquiries and observations proved entirely in vain.

I had heard before my entrance into the Convent, that one of the nuns had made her escape from it during the last war, and once inquired about her of the Superior. She admitted that such was the fact: but I was never able to learn any particulars concerning her name, origin, or manner of escape.

CHAPTER XVII

I AM unable to say how many nuns disappeared while I was in the Convent. There were several. One was a young lady called St. Pierre, I think, but am not certain of her name. There were two nuns by this name. I had known her as a novice with me. She had been a novice about two years and a half before I became one. She was rather large without being tall, and had rather dark hair and eyes. She disappeared unaccountably, and nothing was said of her except what I heard in whispers from a few of the nuns, as we found moments when we could speak unobserved.

Some told me they thought she must have left the Convent; and I might have supposed so, had I not some time afterwards found some of her things lying about, which she would, in such a case, doubtless have taken with her. I had never known anything more of her than what I could observe or conjecture. I had always, however, the idea that her

parents or friends were wealthy, for she sometimes received
clothes and other things which were very rich.

Another nun named St. Paul, died suddenly, but as in
other cases, we knew so little, or rather were so entirely
ignorant of the cause and circumstances, that we could only
conjecture; and being forbidden to speak freely upon that
or any other subject, thought little about it. I have mentioned that a number of veiled nuns thus mysteriously disappeared during my residence among them. I cannot
perhaps recall them all, but I am confident there were as
many as five, and I think more. All that we knew in such
cases was, that one of our number who appeared as usual
when last observed, was nowhere to be seen, and never seen
again. – Mad Jane Ray, on several such occasions, would indulge in her bold, and, as we thought, dangerous remarks.
She had intimated that some of those, who had been for
some time in the Convent, were by some means removed to
make room for new ones; and it was generally the fact,
that the disappearance of one and the introduction of
another into our community, were nearly at the same time.
I have repeatedly heard Jane Ray say, with one of her significant looks, 'When you appear, somebody else disappears.'

It is unpleasant enough to distress or torture one's self;
but there is something worse in being tormented by others,
especially when they resort to force, and show a pleasure in
compelling you, and leave you no hope to escape, or opportunity to resist. I had seen the gags repeatedly in use, and
sometimes applied with a roughness which seemed rather
inhuman; but it is one thing to see and another thing to
feel. They were ready to recommend a resort to compul-
sory measures, and ever ready to run for the gags. These
were kept in one of the community-rooms, in a drawer between two closets; and there a stock of about fifty of them
were always kept in deposit. Sometimes a number of nuns
would prove refractory at a time; and I have seen battles
commenced in which several appeared on both sides. The
disobedient were, however, soon overpowered; and to pre-

vent their screams being heard beyond the walls, gagging commenced immediately. I have seen half a dozen lying gagged and bound at once.

I have been subjected to the same state of involuntary silence more than once; for sometimes I became excited to a state of desperation by the measures used against me, and then conducted myself in a manner perhaps not less violent than some others. My hands have been tied behind me, and a gag put into my mouth, sometimes with such force and rudeness as to separate my lips, and cause the blood to flow freely.

Treatment of this kind is apt to teach submission; and many times I have acquiesced under orders received, or wishes expressed, with a fear of a recurrence to some severe measures.

One day I had incurred the anger of the Superior in a greater degree than usual, and it was ordered that I should be taken to one of the cells. I was taken by some of the nuns, bound and gagged, carried down the stairs into the cellar, and laid upon the floor. Not long afterwards I induced one of the nuns to request the Superior to come down and see me; and on making some acknowledgement, I was released. I will, however, relate this story rather more in detail.

On that day I had been engaged with Jane Ray, in carrying into effect a plan of revenge upon another person, when I fell under the vindictive spirit of some of the old nuns, and suffered severely. The Superior ordered me to the cells, and a scene of violence commenced which I will not attempt to describe, nor the precise circumstances which led to it. Suffice it to say, that after I had exhausted all my strength, by resisting as long as I could, against several nuns, I had my hands drawn behind my back, a leathern band passed first round my thumbs, then round my hands, and then round my waist and fastened. This was drawn so tight that it cut through the flesh of my thumbs, making wounds, the scars of which still remain. A gag was then forced into my mouth, not indeed so violently as it sometimes was, but roughly enough; after which I was taken by main force, and carried down into the cellar, across it almost to the opposite extremity, and brought to the last of the second range of cells on the left hand. The door was opened, and I was thrown in with violence, and left alone, the door being immediately closed, and bolted on the outside. The bare ground was under me, cold and hard as if it had been beaten even. I lay still in the position in which I had fallen, as it would have been difficult for me to move, confined as I was, and exhausted by my exertions; and the shock of my fall, and my wretched state of desperation and fear, disinclined me from any further attempt. I was in almost total darkness, there being nothing perceptible except a slight glimmer of light which came in through the little window far above me.

How long I remained in that condition I can only conjecture. It seemed to me a long time, and must have been two or three hours. I did not move, expecting to die there, and in a state of distress which I cannot describe, from the tight bondage about my hands, and the gag holding my jaws apart to their greatest extent. I am confident I must have died before morning, if, as I then expected, I had been left there all night. By and by, however, the bolt was drawn, the door opened, and Jane Ray spoke to me in a tone of kindness.

She had taken an opportunity to slip into the cellar unnoticed, on purpose to see me. She unbound the gag, took it out of my mouth, and told me she would do anything to get me out of the dungeon. If she had had the bringing of me down she would not have thrust me in so brutally, and she would be resented on those who had. She offered to throw herself upon her knees before the Superior, and beg her forgiveness. To this I would not consent; but told her to ask the Superior to come to me, as I wished to speak to her. This I had no idea she would condescend to do; but Jane had not been long gone before the Superior came, and asked if I repented in the sight of God for what I had done.

I replied in the affirmative; and after a lecture of some length on the pain I had given the Virgin Mary by my conduct, she asked whether I was willing to ask pardon of all the nuns for the scandal I had caused them by my behaviour. To this I made no objection; and I was then released from my prison and my bonds, went up to the community-room, and kneeling before all the sisters in succession, begged the forgiveness and prayers of each.

Among the marks which I still bear of the wounds received from penances and violence, are the scars left by the belt with which I repeatedly tortured myself, for the mortification of my spirit. These are most distinct on my side: for although the band, which was four or five inches in breadth, and extended round the waist, was stuck full of sharp iron points in all parts, it was sometimes crowded most against my side, by resting in my chair, and then the wounds were usually deeper there than anywhere else.

My thumbs were several times cut severely by the tight drawing of the band used to confine my arms; and scars are still visible upon them.

The rough gagging which I several times endured wounded my lips very much; for it was common, in that operation, to thrust the gag hard against the teeth, and catch one or both the lips, which were sometimes cruelly cut. The object was to stop the screams made by the offender, as soon as possible; and some of the old nuns delighted in tormenting us. A gag was once forced into my mouth, which had a large splinter upon it; and this cut through my under lip, in front, leaving to this day a scar about half an inch long. The same lip was several times wounded as well as the other; but one day worse than ever, when a narrow piece was cut off from the left side of it, by being pinched between the gag and the under fore-teeth; and this has left an inequality in it which is still very observable.

One of the most shocking stories I heard, of events that occurred in the nunnery before my acquaintance with it, was the following, which was told me by Jane Ray. What is uncommon, I can fix the date when I heard it. It was on New Year's Day, 1834. The ceremonies, customary in the early part of that day, had been performed; after mass, in the morning, the Superior had shaken hands with all the nuns, and given us her blessing, for she was said to have received power from heaven to do so once a year, and then on the first day of the year. Besides this, cakes, raisins, &c., are distributed to the nuns on that day.

While in the community-room, I had taken a seat just within the cupboard-door, where I often found a partial shelter from observation with Jane, when a conversation incidentally began between us. Our practice often was, to take places there beside one of the old nuns, awaiting the time when she would go away for a little while, and leave us partially screened from the observation of others. On that occasion, Jane and I were left for a time alone, when, after some discourse on suicide, she remarked that three nuns once killed themselves in the Convent. This happened, she said, not long after her reception, and I knew, therefore, that it was several years before I had become a novice. Three young ladies, she informed me, took the veil together, or very near the same time, I am not certain which. I know they have four robes in the Convent, to be worn during the ceremony of taking the veil: but I never have seen more than one of them used at a time.

Two of the new nuns were sisters, and the other their cousin. They had been received but a few days, when information was given one morning, that they had been found dead in their beds, amid a profusion of blood. Jane Ray said she saw their corpses, and that they appeared to have killed themselves by opening veins in their arms with a knife they had obtained, and all had bled to death together. What was extraordinary, Jane Ray added, that she had heard no noise, and she believed nobody had suspected that anything was wrong during the night. St. Hypolite, however, had stated, that she had found them in the morning, after the other nuns had gone to prayers, lying lifeless in their beds.

For some reason or other, their death was not made public; but their bodies, instead of being exhibited in full dress, in the chapel, and afterwards interred with solemnity beneath it, were taken unceremoniously into the cellar, and thrown into the hole I have so often mentioned.

There were a few instances, and only a few, in which we knew anything that was happening in the world; and even then our knowledge did not extend out of the city. I can recall but three occasions of this kind. Two of them were when the cholera prevailed in Montreal; and the other was the election riots. The appearance of the cholera, in both seasons of its ravages, gave us abundance of occupation. Indeed, we were more borne down by hard labour at those times, than ever before or afterwards during my stay. The Pope had given early notice that the burning of wax candles would afford protection from the disease, because, so long as any person continued to burn one, the Virgin Mary would intercede for him. No sooner, therefore, had the alarming disease made its appearance in Montreal, than a long wax candle was lighted in the Convent, for each of the inmates, so that all parts of it in use were artificially illuminated day and night. Thus a great many candles were constantly burning, which were to be replaced from those manufactured by the nuns. But this was a trifle. The Pope's message having been promulgated in the Grey Nunnery, and to the Catholics at large through the pulpit, an extraordinary demand was created for wax candles, to supply which we were principally depended upon. All who could possibly be employed in making them were, therefore, set to work, and I, among the rest, assisted in different departments, and witnessed all.

Numbers of the nuns had long been familiar with the business; for a very considerable amount of wax had been annually manufactured in the Convent; but now the works were much extended, and other occupations in a great degree laid aside. Large quantities of wax were received in the building, which was said to have been imported from

England; kettles were placed in some of the working-rooms, in which it was clarified by heat over coal fires, and when prepared, the process of dipping commenced. The wicks, which were quite long, were placed, hanging upon a reel, taken up and dipped in succession, until after many slow revolutions of the reel, the candles were of the proper size. They were then taken to a part of the room where tables were prepared for rolling them smooth. This is done by passing a roller over them, until they became even and polished; after which they are laid by for sale. These processes caused a constant bustle in several of the rooms; and the melancholy reports from without, of the ravages of the cholera, with the uncertainty of what might be the result with us, notwithstanding the promised intercession of the Virgin, and the brilliant lights constantly burning in such numbers around us, impressed the scenes I used to witness very deeply on my mind. I had very little doubt, myself, of the strict truth of the story we had heard about the security conferred upon those who burnt candles, and yet I sometimes had serious fears arise in my mind. These thoughts, however, I did my utmost to regard as great sins, and evidences of my own want of faith.

It was during that period that I formed a partial acquaintance with several Grey Nuns, who used to come frequently for supplies of candles for their Convent. I had no opportunity to converse with them, except so far as the purchase and sale of the articles they required. I became familiar with their countenances and appearances, but was unable to judge of their characters or feelings. Concerning the rules and habits prevailing in the Grey Nunnery, I therefore remained as ignorant as if I had been a thousand miles off; and they had no better opportunity to learn anything of us, beyond what they could see around them in the room where the candles were sold.

We supplied the Congregational Nunnery also with wax candles, as I before remarked; and in both these institutions, it was understood, a constant illumination was kept up.

Citizens were also frequently running in to buy candles in great and small quantities, so that the business of store-keeping was far more laborious than common.

We were confirmed in our faith in the intercession of the Virgin, when we found that we remained safe from the cholera; and it is a remarkable fact, that not one case of that disease existed in the Nunnery, during either of the seasons in which it proved so fatal in the city.

When the election riots prevailed at Montreal, the city was thrown into general alarm; we heard some reports from day to day, which made us anxious for ourselves. Nothing, however, gave me any serious thoughts, until I saw uncommon movements in some parts of the Nunnery, and ascertained, to my own satisfaction, that there was a large quantity of gunpowder stored in some secret place within the walls, and that some of it was removed, or prepared for use, under the direction of the Superior.

Penances – I have mentioned several penances in different parts of this narration, which we sometimes had to perform. There is a great variety of them; and, while some, though trifling in appearance, became very painful, by long endurance or frequent repetition, others are severe in their nature, and never would be submitted to, unless, through fear of something worse, or a real belief in their efficacy to remove guilt. I will mention here such as I recollect, which can be named without offending a virtuous ear; for some there were, which, although I have been compelled to submit to, either by a misled conscience, or the fear of severe punishment, now that I am better able to judge of my duties, and at liberty to act, I would not mention or describe.

Kissing the floor is a very common penance; kneeling and kissing the feet of the other nuns is another; as are kneeling on hard peas, and walking with them in the shoes. We had repeatedly to walk on our knees through the subterranean passage, leading to the Congregational Nunnery; and sometimes to eat our meals with a rope round our necks.

Sometimes we were fed only with such things as we most disliked. Garlic was given to me on this account, because I had a strong antipathy against it.

Eels were repeatedly given some of us, because we felt an unconquerable repugnance to them, on account of reports we heard of their feeding on dead carcases in the river St. Lawrence. It was no uncommon thing for us to be required to drink the water in which the Superior had washed her feet. Sometimes we were required to brand ourselves with a hot iron, so as to leave scars; at other times, to whip our naked flesh with several small rods, before a private altar, until we drew blood. I can assert, with the perfect knowledge of the fact, that many of the nuns bear the scars of these wounds.

One of the penances was to stand for a length of time with our arms extended, in imitation of the Saviour on the Cross. The *Chemin de la Croix,* or Road to the Cross, is, in fact, a penance, though it consists of a variety of prostrations, with the repetition of many prayers, occupying two or three hours. This we had to perform frequently going to chapel, and falling before each chapelle in succession, at each time commemorating some particular act or circumstance reported of the Saviour's progress to the place of his crucifixion.

Sometimes we were obliged to sleep on the floor in the winter, with nothing over us but a single sheet; and sometimes to chew a piece of window glass to a fine powder, in the presence of the Superior.

We had sometimes to wear a leathern belt stuck full of sharp metallic points, round our waists and the upper part of our arms, bound on so tight that they penetrated the flesh, and drew blood.

Some of the penances were so severe, that they seemed too much to be endured; and when they were imposed, the nuns who were to suffer them showed the most violent repugnance. They would often resist, and still oftener express their opposition by exclamations and screams.

Never, however, was any noise heard from them for a long time, for there was a remedy always ready to be applied in cases of the kind. The gag which was put into the mouth of the unfortunate Saint Frances, had been brought from a place where there were forty or fifty others of different shapes and sizes. These I have seen in their depository, which is a drawer between two closets, in one of the community-rooms. Whenever any loud noise was made, one of these instruments was demanded, and gagging commenced at once. I have known many instances, and sometimes five or six nuns gagged at once. Sometimes they would become so much excited before they could be bound and gagged, that considerable force was necessary to be exerted; and I have seen the blood flowing from mouths into which the gag had been thrust with violence.

Indeed I ought to know something of this department of nunnery discipline; I have had it tried upon myself, and can bear witness that it is not only most humiliating and oppressive, but often extremely painful. The mouth is kept forced open, and the straining of the jaws at their utmost stretch, for a considerable time, is very distressing.

One of the worst punishments which I ever saw inflicted, was that with the cap; and yet some of the old nuns were permitted to inflict it at their pleasure. I have repeatedly known them to go for a cap, when one of our number had transgressed a rule, sometimes though it were a very unimportant one. These caps were kept in a cupboard in the old nuns' room, whence they were brought when wanted.

They were small, made of a reddish looking leather, fitted closely to the head, and fastened under the chin with a kind of buckle. It was the common practice to tie the nun's hands behind, and gag her before the cap was put on to prevent noise and resistance. I never saw it worn by any one for a moment, without throwing them into severe sufferings. If permitted, they would scream in the most shocking manner, and always writhed as much as their confinement would allow. I can speak from personal knowledge of this punishment, as I have endured it more than once; and yet I have no idea of the cause of the pain. I never examined one of the caps, nor saw the inside, for they are always brought and taken away quickly; but although the first sensation was that of coolness, it was hardly put on my head before a violent and indescribable sensation began, like that of a blister, only much more insupportable; and this continued until it was removed. It would produce such an acute pain as to throw us into convulsions, and I think no human being could endure it for an hour. After this punishment, we felt its effect through the system for many days. Having once known what it was by experience, I held the cap in dread, and whenever I was condemned to suffer the punishment again, felt ready to do anything to avoid it. But when tied and gagged, with the cap on my head again, I could only sink upon the floor, and roll about in agony and anguish until it was taken off, and placed in the repository.

This was usually done in about ten minutes, sometimes less, but the pain always continued in my head for several days. I thought that it might take away a person's reason if kept on a much longer time. If I had not been gagged I am sure I should have uttered awful screams. I have felt the effects for a week. Sometimes fresh cabbage leaves were applied to my head to remove it. Having had no opportunity to examine my head, I cannot say more.

Among all the nuns there was the same universal dread and horror of the punishment of the cap. I have heard some of them shriek as loud as their voices would allow them, when they have been told they were to wear it as a penance for some trifling offence of which they have been guilty; formerly, Jane Ray told me, she had known nuns who wore it when I was a novice, who have gone completely off their minds, so severe was the suffering which it inflicted upon that tender part of the body, the head. Blood was often drawn from a few minutes' infliction, and the brain of the strongest person would reel if it was allowed to remain upon the head for a quarter of an hour.

CHAPTER XVIII

THIS punishment was occasionally resorted to for very trifling offences, such as washing the hands without permission;
and it was generally applied on the spot, and before the
other nuns in the community-room.

I have mentioned before, that the country, so far down
as the Three Rivers, is furnished with priests by the Seminary of Montreal; and that these hundred and fifty men are
liable to be occasionally transferred from one station to another. Numbers of them are often to be seen in the streets
of Montreal, as they may find a home in the Seminary.

They are considered as having an equal right to enter the
Black Nunnery whenever they please; and then according
to our oaths, they have complete control over the nuns. To
name all the works of shame of which they are guilty in
that retreat, would require much time and space, neither
would it be necessary to the accomplishment of my object,
which is, the publication of but some of their criminality to
the world, and the development, in general terms, of scenes
thus far carried on in secret within the walls of that Convent, where I was so long an inmate.

Secure against detection by the world, they never believed
that an eye-witness would ever escape to tell of their crimes,
and declare some of their names before the world; but the
time has come, and some of their deeds of darkness must
come to the day. I have seen in the Nunnery, the priests
from more, I presume, than a hundred country places, admitted for shameful and criminal purposes; from St.
Charles, St. Denis, St. Mark's, St. Antoine, Chambly, Bertier
St. John's, &c.

How unexpected to them will be the disclosures I make!
Shut up in a place from which there has been thought to be
but one way of egress, and that the passage to the grave,
they considered themselves safe in perpetrating crimes in

our presence, and in making us share in their criminality as often as they chose, and conducted more shamelessly than even the brutes.

These debauchees would come in without ceremony, concealing their names, both by night and day. Being within the walls of that prison-house of death, where the cries and pains of the injured innocence of their victims would never reach the world, for relief or redress for their wrongs, without remorse or shame, they would glory, not only in sating their brutal passions, but even in torturing, in the most barbarous manner, the feelings of those under their power; telling us at the same time, that this mortifying the flesh was religion, and pleasing to God. The more they could torture us, or make us violate our own feelings, the more pleasure they took in their unclean revelling; and all their brutal obscenity they called meritorious before God.

We were sometimes invited to put ourselves to voluntary sufferings in a variety of ways, not for a penance, but to show our devotion to God. A priest would sometimes say to us—

'Now, which of you have love enough for Jesus Christ to stick a pin through your cheeks?'

Some of us would signify our readiness, and immediately thrust one through up to the head. Sometimes he would propose that we should repeat the operation several times on the spot; and the cheeks of a number of the nuns would be bloody.

There were other acts occasionally proposed and consented to, which I cannot name in a book. Such the Superior would sometimes command us to perform; many of them, things not only useless and unheard of, but loathsome and indecent in the highest possible degree. How they ever could have been invented, I never could conceive. Things were done worse than the entire exposure of the person, though this was occasionally required of several at once in the presence of priests.

The Superior of the Seminary would sometimes come and

inform us that she had received orders from the Pope to request that those nuns who possessed the greatest devotion and faith, should be requested to perform some particular deeds, which she named or described in our presence, but of which no decent or moral person could ever venture to speak. I cannot repeat what would injure any ear, not debased to the lowest possible degree. I am bound by a regard to truth, however, to confess, that deluded women were found among us, who would comply with their requests.

There was a great difference between the characters of our old and new Superiors, which soon became obvious. The former used to say she liked to walk, because it would prevent her from becoming corpulent. She was, therefore, very active, and constantly going about from one part of the Nunnery to another, overseeing us at our various employments. I never saw her in any appearance of timidity; she seemed, on the contrary, bold and masculine, and sometimes much more than that, cruel and cold-blooded, in scenes calculated to overcome any common person. Such a character she had particularly exhibited at the murder of St. Frances.

The new Superior, on the other hand, was so heavy and lame, that she walked with much difficulty, and consequently exercised a less vigilant oversight of the nuns. She was also of a timid disposition, or else had been overcome by some great fright in her past life; for she was apt to become alarmed in the night, and never liked to be alone in the dark. She had long performed the part of an old nun, which is that of a spy upon the younger ones, and was well known to us in that character, under the name of St. Margarite. Soon after her promotion to the station of Superior, she appointed me to sleep in her apartment, and assigned me a sofa to lie upon. One night, while I was asleep, she suddenly threw herself upon me, and exclaimed, in great alarm, 'Oh! mon Dieu! mon Dieu! qu'est-ce que ça?' (Oh! my God! my God! what is that?) I jumped up and looked about the room, but saw nothing, and endeavoured to convince her that there was nothing extraordinary there. But she insisted that a ghost had come and held her bed-curtain, so that she could not draw it. I examined it, and found that the curtain had been caught by a pin in the valence, which had held it back; but it was impossible to tranquilize her for some time. She insisted on my sleeping with her the rest of the night, and I stretched myself across the foot of her bed, and slept there till morning.

During the last part of my stay in the Convent, I was often employed in attending in the hospitals. There are, as I have before mentioned, several apartments devoted to the sick, and there is a physician of Montreal, who attends as ordinary physician to the Convent. It must not be supposed, however, that he knows anything concerning the private hospitals. It is a fact of great importance to be distinctly understood, and constantly borne in mind, that he is never, under any circumstances, admitted into the private hospital rooms. Of those he sees nothing more than any stranger whatever. He is limited to the care of those patients who are admitted from the city into the public hospital, and one of the nuns' hospitals, and these he visits every day. Sick poor are received for charity by the institution, attended by some of the nuns, and often go away with the highest ideas of our charitable characters and holy lives. The physician himself might, perhaps, in some cases, share in the delusion.

I frequently followed Dr. Nelson through the public hospital at the direction of the Superior, with pen, ink and paper, in my hands, and wrote down the prescriptions which he ordered for the different patients. These were afterwards prepared and administered by the attendants. About a year before I left the Convent, I was first appointed to attend the private sick-rooms, and was frequently employed in that duty up to the day of my departure. Of course, I had opportunities to observe the number and classes of patients treated there; and in what I am about to say on this subject, I appeal, with perfect confidence, to any true and competent witness to confirm my words, whenever such a witness may appear. It would be vain for anybody who has merely visited the Convent from curiosity, or resided in it as a novice, to question my declarations. Such a person must necessarily be ignorant of even the existence of the private rooms, unless by someone else. Such rooms, however, there are, and I could relate many things which have passed there during the hours I was employed in them, as I have stated.

One night I was called to sit up with an old nun, named St. Claire, who, in going downstairs, had dislocated a limb, and lay in a sick-room adjoining the hospital. She seemed to be a little out of her head a part of the time, but appeared to be quite in possession of her reason most of the night. It was easy to pretend that she was delirious; but I considered her as speaking the truth, though I felt reluctant to repeat what I heard her say, and excused myself from mentioning it even at confession, on the ground that the Superior thought her deranged.

What led her to some of the most remarkable parts of her conversation was, a motion I made, in the course of the night, to take the light out of her little room into the adjoining apartment, to look once more at the sick persons there. She begged me not to leave her a moment in the dark, for she could not bear it. I have witnessed so many horrid scenes,' said she, 'in this Convent, that I want somebody near me constantly, and must always have a light burning in my room. I cannot tell you,' she added, 'what things I remember, for they would frighten you too much. What you have seen are nothing to them. Many a murder have I witnessed; many a nice young creature has been killed in this Nunnery. I advise you to be very cautious – keep everything to yourself – there are many here ready to betray you.'

What it was that induced the old nun to express so much kindness to me I could not tell, unless she was frightened at the recollection of her own crimes, and those of others, and felt grateful for the care I took of her. She had been one of the night watches, and never before showed me any particular kindness. She did not, indeed, go into detail concerning the transactions to which she alluded, but told me that some nuns had been murdered under great aggravations of cruelty, by being gagged, and left to starve in the cells, or having their flesh burned off their bones with red hot irons.

It was uncommon to find compunction expressed by any of the nuns. Habit renders us insensible to the sufferings of others, and careless about our own sins. I had become so hardened myself, that I find it difficult to rid myself of many of my former false principles and views of right and wrong.

I was one day set to wash some empty bottles from the cellar, which had contained the liquid that was poured into the cemetery there. A number of these had been brought from the corner where so many of them were always to be seen, and placed at the head of the cellar stairs, and there we were required to take them and wash them out. We poured in water and rinsed them; a few drops which got upon our clothes soon made holes in them. I think the liquid was called vitriol, or some such name, and I heard some persons say that it would soon destroy the flesh and even the bones of the dead. At another time, we were furnished with a little of the liquid, which was mixed with a quantity of water, and used in dyeing some cloth black, which was wanted at funerals in the chapel. Our hands were turned very black by being dipped in it, but a few drops of some other liquid were mixed with fresh water, and given us to wash in, which left our skin of a bright red.

The bottles of which I spoke were made of very thick dark-coloured glass, large at the bottom, and, I should say, held something less than a gallon.

I was once much shocked, on entering the room for the examination of conscience, at seeing a nun hanging by a cord from a ring in the ceiling, with her head downward. Her clothes had been tied round with a leathern strap, to keep them in their place, and then she had been fastened in that situation, with her head some distance from the floor. Her face had a very unpleasant appearance, being dark coloured, and swollen by the rushing in of the blood; her hands were tied, and her mouth stopped with a large gag. This nun proved to be no other than Jane Ray, who for some fault had been condemned to this punishment. I could not help noticing how very similar this punishment was to that of the Inquisition.

This was not, however, a solitary case; I heard of numbers who were 'hung', as it was called, at different times; and I saw St. Hypolite and St. Luke undergoing it. This was considered a most distressing punishment; and it was the only one which Jane Ray could not endure, of all she had tried.

Some of the nuns would allude to it in her presence, but it usually made her angry. It was probably practised in the same place while I was a novice, but I never heard or thought of such a thing in those days. Whenever we wished to enter the room for the examination of conscience, we had to ask leave, and, after some delay, were permitted to go, but always under a strict charge to bend the head forward, and keep the eyes fixed upon the floor.

CHAPTER XIX

I often seized an opportunity, when I safely could, to speak a cheering or friendly word to one of the poor prisoners, in passing their cells, on my errands in the cellars. For a time I supposed them to be sisters; but I afterwards discovered that this was not the case. I found that they were always under the fear of suffering some punishment, in case they should be found talking with a person not commissioned to attend them. They would often ask, 'Is not somebody coming?'

I could easily believe what I heard affirmed by others, that fear was the severest of their sufferings. Confined in the dark, in so gloomy a place, with the long arched cellar stretching off this way and that, visited only now and then by a solitary nun, with whom they were afraid to speak their feelings, and with only the miserable society of each other; how gloomy thus to spend day after day, months, and even years, without any prospect of liberation, and liable at any moment to another fate to which the Bishop or Superior might condemn them. But these poor creatures must have known something of the horrors perpetrated in other parts of the building, and could not have been ignorant of the hole in the cellar, which was not far from the cells, and the use to which it was devoted. One of them told me, in confidence, she wished they could get out. They must also have been often disturbed in their sleep, if they ever did sleep, by the numerous priests who passed through the trap-door at no great distance. To be subject to such trials for a single day would be dreadful; but these nuns had them to endure for years.

I often felt much compassion for them, and wished to see them released; but at other times, yielding to the doctrine perpetually taught us in the Convent, that our future happiness would be proportioned to the sufferings we had to undergo in this world, I would rest satisfied that their imprisonment was a real blessing to them.

Others, I presume, participated with me in such feelings. One Sunday afternoon, after we had performed all our ceremonies, and were engaged as usual, at that time, with backgammon and other amusements, one of the young nuns exclaimed, 'Oh! how headstrong are those wretches in the cells, they are as bad as the day they were put in!'

This exclamation was made, as I supposed, in consequence of some recent conversation with them, as I knew her to be particularly acquainted with the older one.

Some of the vacant cells were occasionally used for temporary imprisonment. Three nuns were confined in them, to my knowledge, for disobedience to the Superior, as she called it. They did not join the rest in singing in the evening, being exhausted in the various exertions of the day. The Superior ordered them to sing; and, as they did not comply, after the command had been twice repeated, she ordered them away to the cells.

They were immediately taken down into the cellar, placed in separate dungeons, and the door shut and barred upon them. There they remained through the night, the following day and second night, but were released in time to attend mass on the second morning.

The Superior used occasionally to show something in a glass box, which we were required to regard with the highest degree of reverence. It was made of wax, and called an Agnus Dei. She used to exhibit it to us when we were in a state of grace; that is, after confession and before Sacrament. She said it had been blessed *in the very dish in which our Saviour had eaten*. It was brought from Rome. Every time we kissed it, or even looked at it, we were told it gave a hundred days' release from purgatory to ourselves, or if we did not need it, to our next of kin in purgatory, if not a Protestant. If we had no such kinsman, the benefit was to go to the souls in purgatory not prayed for.

Jane Ray would sometimes say to me, 'Let's kiss it – some of our friends will thank us for it.'

I have been repeatedly employed in carrying dainties of different kinds into the little private room I have mentioned next beyond the Superior's sitting-room, in the second storey, which the priests made their 'Holy Retreat'.

That room I never was allowed to enter. I could only go to the door with a waiter of refreshments, set it down upon a little stand near it, give three raps on the door, and then retire to a distance to await orders. When anything was to be taken away, it was placed on the stand by the Superior, who then gave three raps for me, and closed the door.

The Bishop I saw at least once, when he appeared worse for wine, or something of the kind. After partaking of refreshments in the Convent, he sent for all the nuns, and on our appearance, gave us his blessing, and put a piece of pound cake on the shoulder of each of us, in a manner which appeared singular and foolish.

There are three rooms in the Black Nunnery, which I
never entered. I had enjoyed much liberty, and had seen,
as I supposed, all parts of the building, when one day I
observed an old nun go to a corner of an apartment
near the northern end of the western wing, push the end
of her scissors into a crack in the panelled wall, and pull
out a door. I was much surprised, because I never had conjectured that any door was there; and it appeared, when
I afterwards examined the place, that no indication of it
could be discovered on the closest scrutiny. I stepped
forward to see what was within, and saw three rooms
opening into each other; but the nun refused to admit
me within the door, which she said led to rooms kept as
depositories.

She herself entered and closed the door, so that I could
not satisfy my curiosity; and no occasion presented itself. I
always had a strong desire to know the use of these apartments; for I am sure they must have been designed for some
purpose of which I was intentionally kept ignorant, otherwise they never would have remained unknown to me so
long. Besides, the old nun evidently had some strong reason
for denying me admission, though she endeavoured to
quiet my curiosity.

The Superior, after my admission into the Convent, had
told me I had access to every room in the building; and I
had seen places which bore witness to the cruelties and the
crimes committed under her commands or sanction; but
here was a succession of rooms which had been concealed
from me, and so constructed as if designed to be unknown to
all but a few. I am sure that any person, who might be able
to examine the wall in that place, would pronounce that
secret door a surprising piece of work. I never saw anything
of the kind which appeared to me so ingenious and skilfully
made. I told Jane Ray what I had seen, and she said at
once, 'We will get in and see what is there.' But I suppose
she never found an opportunity.

I naturally felt a good deal of curiosity to learn whether

such scenes as I had witnessed in the death of Saint Frances
were common or rare, and took an opportunity to inquire
of Jane Ray. Her reply was—

'Oh, yes; and there were many murdered while you were
a novice, whom you heard nothing about.'

This was all I ever learnt on this subject; but although I
was told nothing of the manner in which they were killed,
I suppose it to be the same which I had seen practised,
namely, by smothering.

I went into the Superior's parlour one day for something,
and found Jane Ray there alone, looking into a book with
an appearance of interest. I asked her what it was, but she
made some trifling answer, and laid it by as if unwilling to
let me take it. There are two bookcases in the room; one on
the right as you enter the door, and the other opposite, near
the window and the sofa. The former contains the lecture-
books and other printed volumes, the latter seemed to be
filled with note and account books. I have often seen the keys
in the bookcases while I have been dusting the furniture,
and sometimes observed letters stuck up in the room, although I never looked into one, or thought of doing so. We
were under strict orders not to touch any of them, and the
idea of sins and penances was always present in my mind.

Some time after the occasion mentioned, I was sent into
the Superior's room with Jane, to arrange it; and as the
same book was lying out of the case, she said, 'Come let us
look into it.' I immediately consented, and we opened it,
and turned over several leaves. It was about a foot and a half
long, as nearly as I can remember, a foot wide, and about
two inches thick, though I cannot speak with particular precision, as Jane frightened me almost as soon as I touched it,
by exclaiming, 'There, you have looked into it, and if you
tell of me, I will of you.'

The thought of being subjected to a severe penance,
which I had reason to apprehend, fluttered me very much;
and, although I tried to cover my fears, I did not succeed
very well. I reflected, however, that the sin was already

committed, and that it would not be increased if I examined
the book.

I therefore looked a little at several pages, though I still
felt a good deal of agitation. I saw at once that the volume
was a record of the entrance of nuns and novices into the
Convent, and of the births that had taken place in the
Convent. Entries of the last description were made in a
brief manner, on the following plan: I do not give the names
or dates as real, but only to show the form of entering them.

> Saint Mary, delivered of a son, March 16, 1834.
> Saint Clarice,   „   daughter, April 2
> Saint Matilda,   „   daughter, April 30.
> Saint Eunice,   „   son, May 1.
> Saint Martha,   „   daughter, May 10.
> Saint Clotilda,   „   son, May 29.
> Saint Catherine, „   son, June 1.
> Saint Florence,   „   daughter, June 12.
> Saint Bertha,   „   son, June 29.
> Saint Emeline,   „   daughter, July 4.
> Saint Maria,   „   son, July 9.
> Saint Hypolite,   „   daughter, July 20.

So the record went on, enumerating a very large number
of births, which had taken place in the Convent. Fear of
discovery made Jane and myself close the book sooner than
we should have done, if our curiosity could have been grati-
fied without running the risk of being detected. We both
gave utterance to our horror and surprise as we closed that
volume which is a standing proof of the criminality of the
priests and bishops that are now, and have been for years,
the so-called 'spiritual guides' of the poor deluded females
who have sought shelter in the Convent from the sins of
the wicked world without.

No mention was made in the book of the death of the
children, though I well knew not one of them could be living
at that time.

Now I presume that the period the book embraced was

about two years, as several names near the beginning I knew; but I can form only a rough conjecture of the numbers of infants born, and murdered of course, records of which it contained. I suppose the book contained at least one hundred pages, and one fourth were written upon, and that each page contained fifteen distinct records. Several pages were devoted to the list of births. On this supposition there must have been a large number, which I can easily believe to have been born there in the course of two years.

What were the contents of the other books belonging to the same case as that which I had looked into. I have no idea, having never dared to touch one of them; I believe, however, that Jane Ray was well acquainted with them, knowing, as I do, her intelligence and prying disposition. If she could be brought to give her testimony, she would doubtless unfold many curious particulars now unknown.

I am able, in consequence of a circumstance which appeared accidental, to state with confidence the exact number of persons in the Convent one day of the week in which I left it. This may be a point of some interest, as several deaths had occurred since my taking the veil, and many burials had been openly made in the chapel.

I was appointed, at the time mentioned, to lay out the covers for all the inmates of the Convent, including the nuns in the cells. These covers, as I have said before, were linen bands, to be bound around the knives, forks, spoons, and napkins, for eating. These were for all the nuns and novices, and amounted to two hundred and ten. As the number of novices was then about thirty, I know that there must have been at that time about one hundred and eighty veiled nuns.

I was occasionally troubled with a desire of escaping from the Nunnery, and was much distressed whenever I felt so evil an imagination rise in my mind; I believed that it was a sin, a great sin, and did not fail to confess, at every opportunity, that I felt discontent. My confessors informed me that I was beset with evil spirits, and urged me to pray against it. Still, however, every now and then, I would think, 'Oh, if I could get out.'

At length one of the priests to whom I had confessed this sin, informed me, for my comfort, that he had begun to pray to Saint Anthony, and hoped his intercession would, by-and-by, drive away the evil spirit. My desire of escape was partly excited by the fear of bringing an infant to the murderous hands of my companions, or of taking a potion whose violent effects I too well knew.

One evening, however, I found myself more filled with a desire to escape than ever; and what exertions I made to dismiss the thought proved entirely unavailing. During evening prayers I became quite occupied with it; and when the time of meditation arrived, instead of falling into a doze, as I often did, though I was a good deal fatigued, I found no difficulty in keeping awake. When this exercise was over, and the other nuns were about to retire to the sleeping-room, my station being in the private sick-room for the night, I withdrew to my post, which was the little sitting-room adjoining it.

Here, then, I threw myself upon the sofa, and being alone, reflected a few moments on the manner of escaping which had occurred to me. The physician had arrived a little before, at half-past eight; and I had now to accompany him as usual from bed to bed, with pen, ink, and paper, to write down his prescriptions for the direction of the old nun, who was to see them administered.

What I wrote on that evening, I cannot now recollect, as my mind was uncommonly agitated; but my customary way was to note down briefly his orders, in this manner—

> 1 d. salts, St. Matilde.
> 1 blister, St. Genevieve, &c.

I remember that I wrote these orders that evening, and then, having finished the rounds, I returned for a few moments to the sitting-room.

There were two ways of access to the street from those

rooms; first, the more direct, from the passage adjoining the sick-room down stairs, through a door, into the Nunnery-yard, and through a wicker-gate: that is the way by which the physician usually enters at night, and he is provided with a key for that purpose.

It would have been unsafe, however, for me to pass out that way, because a man is kept continually in the yard, near the gate, who sleeps at night in a small hut near the door, to escape whose observation would be impossible. My only hope, therefore, was, that I might gain my passage through the other way, to do which I must pass through the sick-room, then through a passage, or a small room usually occupied by an old nun, another passage and staircase leading down to the yard, and a large gate opening into the cross street. I had no liberty to go beyond the sick-room, and knew that several of the doors might be fastened; still I determined to try; although I have often since been astonished at my boldness in undertaking what would expose me to so many hazards of failure, and to severe punishment if found out.

It seemed as if I acted under some extraordinary impulse, which encouraged me to what I should hardly at any other moment have thought of undertaking. I had sat but a short time upon the sofa, however, before I rose with a desperate determination to make the experiment. I therefore walked hastily across the sick room, passed into the nun's room, walked by her in a great hurry, and almost without giving her time to speak or think, said, 'A message!' and in an instant was through the door, and in the next passage. I think there was another nun with her at the moment; and it is probable that my hurried manner, and prompt intimation that I was sent on a pressing mission to the Superior, prevented them from entertaining any suspicion of my intention. Besides, I had the written orders of the physician in my hand, which may have tended to mislead them; and it was well known to some of the nuns, that I had twice left the Convent, and returned from choice, so that I was probably more likely to be trusted to remain than many of the others.

The passage which I now reached had several doors, with all which I was acquainted; that on the opposite side opened into a community-room, where I should have probably found some of the old nuns at that hour, and they would certainly have stopped me.

On the left, however, was a large door, both locked and barred: but I gave the door a sudden swing, that it might creak as little as possible, being of iron. Down the stairs I hurried, and making my way through the door into the yard, stepped across it, unbarred the great gate, and was at liberty!

Conclusion

THE following circumstances comprise all that is deemed necessary now to subjoin to the preceding narrative.

After my arrival in New York I was introduced to the almshouse, where I was attended with kindness and care, and, as I hoped, was entirely unknown. But when I had been some time in that institution, I found that it was reported that I was a fugitive nun; and not long after, an Irish woman, belonging to the house, brought me a secret message, which caused me some agitation.

I was sitting in the room of Mrs. Johnson, the matron, engaged in sewing, when that Irish woman, employed in the institution, came in and told me that Mr. Conroy was below, and had sent to see me. I was informed that he was a Roman priest, who often visited the house, and he had a particular wish to see me at that time; having come, as I believe, expressly for that purpose. I showed unwillingness to comply with such an invitation, and did not go.

The woman told me, further, that he sent me word that I need not think to avoid him, for it would be impossible for me to do so. I might conceal myself as well as I could, but I should be found and taken. No matter where I went, or what hiding-place I might choose, I should be known; and I had better come at once. He knew who I was; and he was authorized to take me to the Sisters of Charity, if I should prefer to join them. He would promise that I might stay with them if I chose, and be permitted to remain in New York. He sent me word further that he had received full power and authority over me from the Superior of the Hotel Dieu Nunnery at Montreal, and was able to do all that she could do, as her right to dispose of me at her will had been imparted to him by a regular writing received from Canada. This was alarming information for me, in the weakness in which I was at that time. The woman added, that the same authority had been given to all the priests; so that go where I might I should meet men informed about me and my escape, and fully empowered to seize me whenever they could, and convey me back to the Convent from which I had escaped.

Under these circumstances, it seemed to me that the offer to place me among the Sisters of Charity, with permission to remain in New York, was mild and favourable. However, I had resolution enough to refuse to see Priest Conroy.

Not long afterwards I was informed, by the same messenger, that the priest was again in the building, and repeated his request. I desired one of the gentlemen connected with the institution, that a stop might be put to such messages as I wished to receive no more of them. A short time after, however, the woman told me that Mr. Conroy wished to inquire of me, whether my name was not St. Eustace while a nun, and if I had not confessed to Priest Kelly in Montreal. I answered that it was all true, for I had confessed to him a short time while in the Nunnery. I was then told again that the priest wanted to see me, and I sent back word that I would see him in the presence of Mr. T— or Mr. S—; which, however, was not agreed to; and I was afterwards informed, that Mr. Conroy, the Roman priest, spent an hour in the room and a passage where I had frequently been; but, through the mercy of God, I was employed at another place at that time, and had no occasion to go where I should have met him. I afterwards repeatedly heard that Mr. Conroy continued to visit the house, and to ask for me; but I never saw him. I once had determined to leave the institution, and go to the Sisters of Charity; but circumstances occurred which gave me time for further reflection; and I was saved from the destruction to which I should have been exposed.

As the period of my accouchement approached, I sometimes thought that I should not survive it; and then the recollection of the dreadful crimes I had witnessed in the Nunnery would come upon me very powerfully, and I would think it a solemn duty to disclose them before I died. To have a knowledge of those things, and leave the world without making them known, appeared to me like a great sin, whenever I could divest myself of the impression made upon me by the declarations and arguments of the Superior, nuns, and priests, of the duty of submitting to everything, and the necessary holiness of whatever they did or required.

The evening but one before the period which I anticipated with so much anxiety, I was sitting alone, and began to indulge in reflections of this kind. It seemed to me that I must be near the close of my life, and I determined to make a disclosure at once. I spoke to Mrs. Ford, a woman whose character I respected, a nurse in the hospital, number twenty-three. I informed her that I had no expectation of living long, and had some things on my mind which I wished to communicate before it should be too late. I added, that I should prefer telling them to Mr. T—, the chaplain! of which she approved, as she considered it a duty to do so, under those circumstances. I had no opportunity, however, to converse with Mr. T— at that time, and, probably, my purpose of disclosing the facts already given in this book, would never have been executed, but for what subsequently took place.

It was alarm which led me to form such a determination; and when the period of trial had been safely passed, and I had a prospect of recovery, anything seemed to me more unlikely than that I should make this exposure.

I was then a Roman Catholic, at least a great part of my time; and my conduct, in a great measure, was according to the faith and motives of a Roman Catholic. Notwithstanding what I knew of the conduct of so many of the priests and nuns, I thought that it had no effect on the sanctity of the church, or the authority or effects of the acts performed by the former at the mass, confession, &c. I had such a regard for my vows as a nun, that I considered my hand as well as my heart irrevocably given to Jesus Christ, and could never have allowed any person to take it. Indeed, to this day I feel an instinctive aversion to offering my hand, or taking the hand of another person, even as an expression of friendship.

I also thought that I might soon return to the Catholics, although fear and disgust held me back. I had now that infant to think for, whose life I had happily saved by my timely escape from the Nunnery; what its fate might be, in case it should ever fall into the power of the priests, I could not tell.

I had, however, reason for alarm. Would a child, destined to destruction, like the infants I had seen baptized and smothered, be allowed to go through the world unmolested, a living memorial of the truth of crimes long practised in security, because never exposed? What pledges could I get to satisfy me, that I, on whom her dependence must be, would be spared by those who, I had reason to think, were wishing then to sacrifice me? How could I trust the helpless infant in hands which had hastened the baptism of many such, in order to hurry them into the secret pit in the cellar? Could I suppose that *Father Phelan, Priest of the Parish Church of Montreal*, would see *his own child* growing up in the world, and feel willing to run the risk of having the truth exposed? What would I expect, especially from him, but the utmost rancour, and the most determined enmity, against the innocent child and its abused and defenceless mother?

Yet, my mind would sometimes still incline to the opposite direction, and indulge the thought, that perhaps the
only way to secure heaven to us both, was to throw ourselves
back into the hands of the church, to be treated as she
pleased. – When, therefore, the fear of immediate death
was removed, I renounced all thoughts of communicating
the substance of the facts of this volume. It happened, however, that my danger was not passed. I was soon seized with
very alarming symptoms; then my desire to disclose my
story revived.

I had before had an opportunity to speak in private with
the chaplain; but, as it was at a time when I supposed myself out of danger, I had deferred for three days my proposed communication, thinking that I might yet avoid it
altogether. When my symptoms, however, became more
alarming, I was anxious for Saturday to arrive, the day
which I had appointed; and when I had not the opportunity, on that day, which I desired, I though it might be too
late. I did not see him till Monday, when my prospects of
surviving were very gloomy, and I then informed him that I
wished to communicate to him a few secrets, which were
likely otherwise to die with me. I then told him, that while a
nun, in the Convent of Montreal, I had witnessed the murder
of a nun, called Saint Frances, and of at least one of the
infants which I have spoken of in this book. I added some
few circumstances, and I believe disclosed, in general terms,
some of the crimes I knew of in that Nunnery.

My anticipations of death proved to be unfounded; for my
health afterwards improved, and had I not made the confessions on that occasion, it is very possible I might never have
made them. I, however, afterwards, felt more willing to listen to instruction, and experienced friendly attentions from
some of the benevolent persons around me, who, taking an
interest in me on account of my darkened understanding,
furnished me with the Bible, and were ever ready to counsel
me when I desired it.

I soon began to believe that God might have intended

that his creatures should learn his will by reading his word, and taking upon them the free exercise of their reason, and acting under responsibility to him.

It is difficult for one who has never given way to such arguments and influences as those to which I had been exposed, to realize how hard it is to think aright, after thinking wrong. The Scriptures always affect me powerfully when I read them; but I feel that I have but just begun to learn the great truths, in which I ought to have been early and thoroughly instructed. I realize, in some degree, how it is that the Scriptures render the people of the United States so strongly opposed to such doctrines as are taught in the Black and Congregational Nunneries of Montreal. The priests and nuns used often to declare that of all heretics, the children from the United States were the most difficult to be converted; and it was thought a great triumph when one of them was brought over to 'the true faith'. The first passage of Scripture that made any serious impression upon my mind, was the text on which the chaplain preached on the Sabbath after my introduction to the house. – 'Search the Scriptures.'

THE CADIERE CASE

being a true account of

the charge brought by

MISS CATHARINE CADIERE

against the Jesuit

FATHER JEAN-BAPTISTE GIRARD

at Toulon

and including details of her
Seduction, her Possession by
Devils, the Abortion she
suffered and the Scourgings
she received

THE case of Cadiere versus Girard was one of the greatest and most vehemently discussed scandals of the eighteenth century. It was a case which hit at the very foundations of contemporary morality and, perhaps more importantly, which demonstrated the potential for evil within that currently most sacrosanct of institutions, the Catholic Church. The very nature of the case touched upon an area of life – sexuality – which people did not wish to discuss openly and, to make matters worse, it imputed sexual offences to a respected member of the Jesuit community. In other words, the case was an explosive amalgam of sexuality and religion at a time when all young women of any social position were assumed to be chaste and all priests were known to be celibate.

In many ways, the case would have been much more straightforward and even acceptable to the public at large had it been a simple affair of seduction and debauchery. But it was not. Seduction there certainly was, but so entangled with the mystique of sanctity and religion, so coloured by devil possession and spiritual passion that it was impossible for all but a few people to regard the case unemotionally or with any degree of objectivity. The power of the church was so great and the universality of belief so complete that, in the event, the case became a simple one of a young woman's word against the united might of the church.

In the present century, it is difficult to imagine the force once wielded by the church, particularly in a traditionally Catholic country such as France which was the setting for the extraordinary events of the Cadiere Case. At that time, however, the church was not only a political power, but an important and influential part of everyday life. Priests were very special people. They wielded an accepted authority, enjoyed unusual privileges by virtue of their learning and their intimate connection with God. To the average man or woman, they represented the ultimate power, for they had the ability to cut a person off from God, either by withholding absolution or by threatening excommunication. Today, such things seem relatively unimportant to the majority, but at the time these were very genuine threats. There was no question in the average believer's mind that he could be punished for his sins, that he might spend eternity burning in the fires of hell. Simply because the 'punishments' meted out by the church were intangible and forthcoming, they were a greater source of fear. A civil crime, on the other hand, could be punished, that punishment could be endured and then forgotten, but a spiritual 'crime' had eternal repercussions. In this lay the source of the church's very real and extensive power over individual lives.

Thus the most extraordinary aspects of the Cadiere Case are explained. As we shall see, the victim of this strange affair never really stood a chance. Evidence was obviously falsified, witnesses were bribed and intimidated quite openly. Yet though this was known and recognized, only the very brave spoke out against it simply because to accuse a priest or even to believe him capable of such wrongdoing was to risk the wrath of God, as interpreted by the priests. Further, to believe evil of a priest was quite alien. Such men were practically divine to their ignorant parishioners. They arbitrated on the sins and doubts of mere mortals and this very privilege somehow set them above temptation so that a corrupt church was unthinkable. Above all, everybody had a vested interest. If a chink were found in the church's armour then not only would its power be effectively questioned but ungodliness would become rife. For, at the time, religion was very much an active war against the Devil, and if the church were weakened people genuinely believed that he would take over. Similarly, people were hesitant in their criticisms of the church simply because it was the sole key to their salvation. Without the church there was only purgatory both now and in the life hereafter. That was a risk that only the very bravest men were prepared to take.

The church's power, then, was absolute and intensely real to the people involved in the Cadiere Case. To usurp the church's power, i.e. the protection and privilege of a man of God for sexual or indeed any ends, was such a heinous crime that it was unthinkable. No worse charge could be laid against a priest, and if it were persisted in, a great many heads would roll. It is against this complex background of religious power that the Cadiere Case must be considered for, when all is said and done, it is the unquestioned inviolability of the priesthood which enabled the perpetuation of the events in the first place and which permitted the extraordinary judicial chicanery which attended the affair once it was made public.

In a pamphlet published in Edinburgh soon after 1730,* based on the deposition of Catharine Cadiere's lawyer, the protagonists in the affair were described as follows:

'Miss Catharine Cadiere, daughter of Mr. Joseph Cadiere, Merchant of the City of Toulon, and of Elizabeth Pomet, was born 12th November, 1709. Her father dying when she was yet in her infancy, left his widow with three boys besides this daughter, a fortune suitable to their rank. The widow educated her family to virtue with the greatest care; the eldest son, at his mother's solicitation, married; the second took the habit of St. Dominic; the third went into Ecclesiastical Orders; and the daughter, who was the youngest, continued under the tender and affectionate care of her good

* The case quickly attracted the attention of publishers in various countries. Printers in Toulon and Aix were quickly busy bringing out folio volumes in 1731, one such being in two volumes: *Recueil Général des Pièces concernant Le Procez entre La Demoiselle Cadière et le Père Girard*. The following year there was a book about the case issued in Cologne. The publishers of the present work have had access to these, and to the smaller work in English issued by Allan Ramsay and Gavin Hamilton at Edinburgh, which quickly ran into at least ten impressions! The title of this is *The Case of Mary Catharine Cadiere against the Jesuit Father John Baptist Girard*.

mother. The chief directors of her conscience were Mr.
Giraud, Rector of the Cathedral Church of Toulon, a gentleman distinguished by his merit and virtue, and Mr.
d'Oulonne, Vicar of the Parish of St. Louis. Under their
direction, this young lady became a pattern of virtue, and
the bent of her mind to piety and devotion was so strong
that she refused several very honourable and very advan-
tageous matches. At the age of eighteen she still retained
that simplicity, that innocence of manners which is so rarely
found in other girls even of seven years old.

'Such was the character of Miss Catharine Cadiere when
Father John Baptist Girard, the Jesuit, arrived at Toulon in
the month of April 1728 as Rector of the Royal Seminary
of Chaplains of the Navy. The great reputation he had
acquired at Aix, where he was admired both as a Preacher
and as a Confessor, together with that air of modesty, aus-
terity and mortification which then appeared in his countenance and through his whole behaviour, soon drew to him
a great number of penitents; and amongst the rest, Miss
Cadiere was induced to make a choice of him chiefly because Mr. d'Oulonne, then her director, was so much employed that she could not go to confession so often as she
inclined.'

From the very outset it seems inevitable that Catharine
Cadiere and Father Girard should be drawn together. She
was, from all accounts, an unusually devout girl. She had
refused offers of marriage in order to devote herself to God.
She was quiet and good-mannered. She went to church more
often than many would consider strictly necessary, but this
was regarded as being in her favour rather than any criti-
cism of her. It was widely known that she was thinking of
taking the veil. The Cadieres were a demonstrably religious
family, and it would have surprised no one if young
Catharine had followed her brothers into the church. In a
small way, she was a famous girl, her devotion having
singled her out both in the eyes of her religious directors and
the townspeople.

Father Girard, on the other hand, was a celebrated religious figure. He came to Toulon with a ready-made reputation as a devout and effective man of God. His post, however, would make less demands on his time than that of Catharine Cadiere's director who had a parish to serve. Undoubtedly Catharine Cadiere was brought to his attention as being a remarkable girl who could benefit from his superior experience and knowledge. In this connection, the fact that he was a Jesuit would also play an important part. The Jesuits were known for their strictness and theological wisdom. They were also, by avowed intent, the recruiters of converts and the saint-makers of the Catholic Church. Catharine Cadiere obviously needed more instruction. Her local priest had undoubtedly taken her as far along the path to perfection as he could. Her confessor was, apart from anything else, too busy to be able to devote to her as much time as she required. Father Girard, with his excellent background, was obviously the ideal choice for her confessor, a man with the necessary time, knowledge and wisdom to assist her in her devotion to God.

To Catharine, he must have seemed the answer to her prayers, a man who could reveal more of the religious mysteries to her, who could aid her spiritual quest. To Father Girard, Catharine must have seemed an exciting challenge. A young girl, reputedly exceptionally devout, whom he could not only teach and instruct but, if she responded to his evangelical approach, who would be a veritable triumph for him, certain to bring him to the favourable attention of his superiors.

Unfortunately, however, for Catharine Cadiere and Father Girard himself, his interest in the saintly young girl was not entirely spiritual. Whether he was immediately attracted to her, or whether his sexual interest developed as the possibilities of the situation dawned on him, is not known. What is certain is that he took a most lively interest not only in Catharine but at least six other young women as well. He was a priest, it seemed, with a special talent for

helping the young ladies of Toulon to find spiritual fulfil-
ment and even ecstasy. As such he was revered, but it later
transpired that he was also a man with a most unpriestlike
interest in his penitents.

'Under his direction she continued two years and an half,
during the first of which nothing extraordinary passed; only
she found he was inquisitive about the conditions and circumstances of herself and her family, and observed that
he treated her with a particular regard, which she then
attributed only to his charity as her confessor. He frequently
told her at confession that God required something more
from her, that He had great designs upon her, and that she
ought to give herself entirely up to God; sometimes adding,
"Will you not give yourself up to me?" The pretended piety
of the confessor, and the real simplicity of the penitent, did
not suffer her to discern the venom concealed in the last
expression.'

From these remarks it is obvious that Father Girard's
plans were carefully laid and that he took considerable
pains not to attract undue attention even on the part of his
victim. Catharine Cadiere was, obviously, an ideal candi-
date for his plans. She was fatherless. Two of her brothers
were safely bestowed in the church where they could present no threat to Girard should anything go wrong. The
other brother played no part in any proceedings connected
with the case, from which we may deduce that he was probably no longer in Toulon or so busy with his own concerns
that he, too, had no potential as an opponent. Catharine's
natural and widely acknowledged piety gave Girard every
opportunity to see and talk with her, while her genuine
religious sincerity meant that she had complete trust in her
fifty-year-old confessor.

In order for Girard's plans to come to fruition it was obviously essential that he see as much of Catharine Cadiere as
possible, so that she might come directly under his influence
and learn to trust him no matter what might occur. However, they might only meet in church and at the Jesuit Con-

vent where Catharine could legitimately go for instruction
and advice and this, as the following passage reveals, was
not sufficient for Girard.

'After about a year's direction, being one day in the parlour of the Jesuit Convent with Father Girard, he upbraided
her in an obliging manner for being so unkind as not to
send for him during an illness of which she was just recovered, and said to her, "Will you not for once give yourself
up to me?" Then stooping down and putting his mouth
close to hers, he breathed upon her, which had such a powerful effect upon the young lady's mind that she was immediately transported with love and consented to give herself up
to him.'

Here is the first evidence of enchantment or possession
which was to become such a feature of the case and which
today presents its most difficult aspect. In the subsequent
inquiry into their relationship, it was claimed that Father
Girard enchanted the girl and caused her to undergo visions
and fits. These are traced back to the incident in the parlour
when Girard's breath is supposed to have enthralled
Catharine Cadiere. Miss Cadiere's position was, at the time
of her testimony, such a precarious one that it was obviously
in her interests for her to claim that she had been from the
very beginning under some sort of spell. And, in a sense,
she was.

After a year of intense religious association with Girard,
it would indeed have been strange if she did not find herself
drawn to him. Further, she was a totally innocent girl whose
body must have been subject to the same demands as those
of less pious girls. Undoubtedly Girard embraced her, perhaps even kissed her, thus awakening in her a sensuality
and romantic excitement which she would not be able to
understand. His actions were 'explained' by the joy he felt
at hearing her promise to give herself up to God – or rather
to him. From that day on he had complete control of
Catharine Cadiere. He had awakened in her feelings with
which her background and religious devotions had not

equipped her to cope, but at the same time he had success-
fully overcome any natural objections she may have had by
setting his seduction, which now began in earnest, within a
context of unimpeachable respectability – the love of God.
The two kinds of love, the physical and the spiritual, were
completely intermingled in Catharine's mind to such an
extent that she may well have thought, during the events
that followed, that she was truly giving herself to God and
not to a man in a priest's habit.

Girard instructed her to make daily confession, a privilege granted only to those who are particularly favoured by
the church, but he prudently requested her to make her
confession at a different church each day so that the privilege granted to her would not be remarked upon. It would
appear certain that he usually met Catharine at a prearranged church and heard her confession. Thus he had
daily access to his potential saint, and at the same time informed her that she would soon be visited by visions and
ecstasies which would reveal God's intentions for and to
her. These visions, however, when they came, were to be
revealed only to Girard himself. They were a secret and a
bond between them.

At this time, Catharine Cadiere underwent what we
would now call a severe crisis of conscience. She realized
that her interest in her confessor was not primarily spiritual
and this, in one so previously devout, would obviously
cause considerable distress. She found it impossible to pray,
and this, plus her passion for Girard himself, she confessed to him. The only proper course open to Girard was
to hand Catharine over to another confessor, but that
was not at all congenial to his plans. Instead, he informed
her:

'That prayer is only the means of coming to God, but that
when we are once arrived there, and united to Him, it is no
longer necessary. The love you have for me ought to give
you no concern. It is the pleasure of our gracious God that
we two should be united. I carry you in my bosom and in

my heart. You are henceforth one with me, and the soul of my soul.'

His direction concerning prayer is a complete contradiction of all the tenets of the church, and his encouragement of her feelings towards himself not only confirms his intentions but also counts as a grievous sin. However, it made sense to Catharine Cadiere, who was by now completely suggestible and virtually putty in Girard's hands.

His next important move came at the end of 1729 when, at his request, Catharine revealed that she had had a vision of a soul in torment, and had heard a voice telling her that if she wished to save this soul she should allow herself to be possessed of the Devil for one year. This extraordinary idea could easily have been planted in Catharine's mind by the wily Jesuit. The idea of saving a soul from torment would obviously appeal to a girl with sincere religious impulses and the fact of Devil possession would be an almost foolproof means of explaining highly irregular and attention-catching behaviour. Not surprisingly, Girard instructed Catharine that she must obey the vision in every particular.

'During her possession, Miss Cadiere was tormented with frightful and horrid apparitions and frequent convulsions, in the fits of which she never opened her mouth but to pour out horrible blasphemies and imprecations; and when her two brothers, the clergyman and the Jacobin, prayed for her relief, she cursed them bitterly and complained that they did but increase her agony. While she was in this condition, she thought that the Devil told her that Father Girard's person was charmed, and that he had entered into a compact with him to enable him to be an admired preacher, on condition that he should deliver to him as many souls as he could.'

The revelation of Girard's own pact with the Devil is obviously an attempt on Catharine Cadiere's part to discredit her confessor after the event. If she had had any such suspicion at the time, it is only reasonable to think that she would have told someone and would have been brought to her senses. The fact remains that she was a willing, if deluded, partner in these visions and only later laid the responsibility for them with Girard.

This extraordinary state of affairs was, however, kept a strict secret. The family were persuaded by Girard not to mention a word about Catharine's strange state of mind, and the only other people who learned of it were the select circle of women whom Girard regularly confessed and who were, subsequent evidence suggested, themselves experiencing similar manifestations of 'heavenly' love.

Not surprisingly, these fits and visions caused Catharine Cadiere to be confined to her room and this was exactly what Girard had wanted. Flagrantly breaking a law of his order which states that no Jesuit priest may visit a woman alone, he called daily upon the Cadieres and spent long hours locked up alone with Catharine. To her family, he presented her as a possible saint in the making, one who needed his constant personal surveillance and guidance.

For a period of seven months, beginning in December 1729 and lasting until June 1730, Catharine Cadiere was a prey to visions and ecstatic trances. For a fortnight during Lent, she was quite unable to keep any food at all in her stomach, and was the recipient, moreover, of extraordinary and painful stigmata. After one vision, a wound appeared in her side, a little below her breast and this, Girard announced, was nothing less than the 'print of our Saviour's wound'.

'She continued from Maundy Thursday till the Saturday following in a trance, without motion, and under a total suspension of all her senses, with one of these stigmas open and bleeding in each of her hands and feet, besides that which she had before on her side; her face also being marked with drops of blood which fell from a bloody crown that appeared on her head . . .

'The pain which these stigmas gave Miss Cadiere made her endeavour to ease it by plasters; but Father Girard sharply reproved her for so doing, telling her they were divine wounds and marks that needed no human remedy, made her pull off the plasters, and then kissed the marks with great veneration, as he did frequently afterwards; especially the stigma on her side which he kissed with the utmost sensuality, and under pretence that he had one of the same kind within, frequently clapped his side close to Miss Cadiere's.'

These extraordinary occurrences, however, only had one purpose – to give Father Girard a remarkable excuse to be locked up alone with Catharine Cadiere, thus enabling him effectively to seduce her.

'Father Girard, being locked up alone with Miss Cadiere in her chamber, when a violent fit of possession of ecstasy took away her senses, laid hold of that opportunity to satisfy his brutal appetite by committing upon his penitent the most infamous crimes; so that when she came to herself, she often found herself in very indecent postures, and her confessor by her with such tokens as left no room to doubt that he had accomplished his villainous purpose. As her fits and trances were very frequent, he had opportunities enough to indulge his lust; and whenever the forementioned circumstances, or the criminal liberties he took with her, obliged her to represent to him the doubts and uneasiness of her mind, he endeavoured to remove her scruples by telling her that it was the pleasure of their gracious God ... When she acquainted La Guiol, Father Girard's confidante, with what he did to her, she laughed in her face and said she must be very simple, or rather very silly, to fancy there was any harm in that. Miss Cadiere also told all the other penitents that were Father Girard's favourites what passed between him and her and they in return entrusted her with the secret of his taking the same liberties with them.'

That sexual intercourse took place on these occasions there is absolutely no doubt, as will be revealed later. Nor was Catharine Cadiere the only favoured lady. Through the good offices of Jean-Baptiste Girard, there were at least seven young Toulon women who received the love of God in a manner which can only be described as blasphemous. As though that were not enough in itself, it appears that Girard was not content with straightforward sexuality. Subsequent events revealed him as something of a sadist and, again, the extraordinary position of religious and emotional dependence into which he had so skilfully manoeuvred Catharine Cadiere enabled him to get away with even greater excesses.

During the course of her 'possession', Girard informed Catharine that she would levitate. This she refused to do. In her testimony she claimed that she was so afraid that she clung on to the furniture. Obviously, no matter what extraordinary psychological powers Girard possessed, he could not make his penitent float above the ground. The events which followed this extraordinary attempt, however, suggest that he always intended that Catharine should fail in this feat of religious possession. Indeed, we may assume that he had chosen the idea of levitation simply because it was beyond realization. Catharine herself, however, may well have believed that some force was trying to lift her from the ground, for by then she must have been in a very disturbed mental state and, besides, her devotion to Girard would surely make anything seem possible.

Whatever the explanation, Catharine did not levitate, and Girard left her apparently in a state of anger. She was, he said, not giving herself up to the will of God. One of his predictions had not come true, but since he only said what God revealed to him, obviously Catharine was at fault. The next time she received confession, he informed her that he would visit her the next day and would prescribe a just penance. Catharine left, broken in spirit, filled with a sense of her own worthlessness. She had failed not only God but her lover as well. She deserved to be punished.

'Accordingly next morning he comes to her apartment, locks her chamber door, makes her kneel down before him and, with a scourge in his hand, thus addresses her: "The justice of God requires that seeing you refused to be clothed with His gifts, you should be stripped naked. You deserve that all the world should be witness of your shame, but your gracious God consents that no other should see it besides these walls and me, who cannot speak. But first of all, swear fidelity to me that you will keep this an inviolable secret, for, my dear child, it would ruin me should you speak of it." The poor young lady, not suspecting his design, promised him secrecy, whereupon he ordered her to get upon the bed, put a cushion under her elbows to raise her up and threw her skirts and shift over her head. Whereupon he drew back his arm and delivered a few lashes on her bare flesh with his scourge, and then tenderly kissed the part that he had whipped. After which he made her rise from the bed and kneel once more before him. In this posture, he told her God was not yet satisfied, and that she must necessarily strip naked. Frightened at such an injunction, she screamed out and fainted away; but as soon as she recovered, he undressed her to her shirt and embraced her. Soon he commenced to run his hands beneath her shirt, caressing her bare flesh, feeling her breasts and thus inducing in her a transport which quite overcame her powers of resistance so that he was enabled to ravish and have his way with her.'

Not only does this account reveal the sadistic tendencies in Girard's nature, for the whipping had direct and obvious sexual connotations for him, but by enjoining Catharine to silence, he betrays an indisputable awareness of what he is doing and of its criminal aspects.

Some three months after the beginning of Catharine Cadiere's 'possession', i.e., after their first solitary meeting, Catharine told Girard that she had missed two of her monthly periods. All the evidence points to the fact that Catharine was telling the truth when she claimed, in her deposition, that she did not understand the significance of this cessation of menstruation. She mentioned the occurrence to Girard simply because she thought it was connected with her religious experiences.

'Frightened at this, he persuaded his penitent that her blood was inflamed, and that in order to temper it, she would drink every day for a week a porringer of water wherein he would put some refreshing powders. She, who knew nothing of the matter, answered she would do what he thought fit; and thereupon this charitable director went every day down to the kitchen to fetch her a porringer of water, which he would not allow either her maid or her mother even to touch, much less to carry to Miss Cadiere, to whom he administered it with his own hands, after having put into it a little powder which gave it a reddish tincture. This draught repeated every day for about a week, occasioned a loss of blood, which continued running for several days, and made her void a small lump of flesh or clotted blood. One day that she had made a whole pot full of blood, Father Girard carried it twice to the window and with curious eyes examined the contents; and when Miss Cadiere bid the maid throw it out the window, and she was carrying it away for that purpose, he was very angry with his penitent for trusting a secret of that consequence to a servant, and cried out, "Was there ever anything so imprudent?"'

The abortion greatly weakened Catharine Cadiere and her family became alarmed for her health. Mme. Cadiere wished to call in a physician, but bowed to Girard's authority when he impressed upon her that Catharine's poor health was the result of divine powers and could not be aided by medical arts. It must have been obvious, however, even to Father Girard, that the situation could not continue as it was, and he therefore wrote to the Abbess of the Convent of St. Clare at Ollioules, beseeching her to take Catharine into her house. Catharine's devout reputation had already reached the ears of the Abbess who readily agreed to give her a lodging. Consequently, Catharine was sent there on 6th June, 1730, accompanied by a letter of introduction from Girard which not only painted his charge in saint-like terms, but also instructed the Abbess not to open any letters which might pass between himself and Catharine Cadiere. This was a direct infringement of the rules of the Convent, but Girard succeeded in convincing the Abbess that frequent letters were essential and would deal only with spiritual matters connected with the confessional.

To make it easier for him to visit her, Girard quickly set about getting himself authorized to confess her at the Convent which he began to visit regularly. There were, however, few occasions when they could enjoy the privacy of Catharine's own bedroom. Mostly they met in the Convent parlour, separated by a grill. This was insupportable to Girard, who gave Catharine a knife with which she was able to unlatch the grill from her side, thus enabling her confessor to kiss her and fondle her body.

Almost immediately upon her arrival at the Convent, Catharine Cadiere began to experience more fits, convulsions and trances. Girard was sent for at once. He arrived at St. Clare, however, before the message had been delivered, claiming that God had sent him to witness the transfiguration of his penitent. Obviously, these events had been prearranged between Catharine and himself and this convenient visitation enabled him to spend the day locked up in a cell with Catharine. He became, in fact, a regular visitor to the Convent, and wrote to her at least once a day. Meanwhile, the extraordinary trances and visions continued to such a degree that news of them quickly spread and Catharine Cadiere became known as the Saint of Ollioules.

It was at this point in their strange relationship that Father Girard determined to send his supposedly saintly mistress away, either to Prémole or to Lyons. He frequently said at Ollioules that Catharine Cadiere had done enough good there and should now move on to edify other religious houses with her presence. It is difficult to discover the exact reason for this sudden reversal of his intentions. It has been suggested that he had grown tired of his mistress. Certainly the difficulties and dangers of seeing her at Ollioules, and the fact that after his first visit the Abbess refused to allow him to shut himself up in Catharine's cell, may well have dampened his ardour. But it is surely also significant that his personal interest in her began to wane just as her fame as a supposed saint began to spread. It may well be that he feared discovery and wished to get her as far away as possible. In that way he would undoubtedly have been able to bask in the reputation of a saint-maker without running the now overt risk of being discovered in his true capacity.

Whatever his reasons, his plan was not to mature. News of his intention to send Catharine Cadiere away reached the ears of the Bishop of Toulon who immediately took steps to frustrate the plan. Such a remarkable case of sanctity in his Diocese should not, he believed, be transplanted to other parts of the country. He intended that any glory should remain in his parish. Consequently, he wrote personally to Catharine, ordering her not to obey Father Girard's instructions and even forbidding her to make confession to him. A few days later he sent a coach to St. Clare's and had her escorted to the house of a friend at La Bastide, just outside Toulon.

Before she left, however, Catharine must have communicated this unexpected and, from her point of view, disastrous news to Girard. He immediately did two things. Firstly, he sent one of his favoured lady penitents to St. Clare with a note requesting Catharine to return all his letters to him. This she did without question. Next he wrote her a letter which purports to be a reply to her request that she be allowed to take a new confessor. This Girard readily agrees to, backing down from this 'exalted' position with true Jesuit humility and grace – or so it was intended to seem.

'The Bishop, having removed Miss Cadiere from the direction of Father Girard, placed her under the care of Father Nicholas, who was just then appointed Prior of the bare-footed Carmelites at Toulon, to whom he said, "I entrust you with the Saint of Ollioules"; and it was by the Bishop's express order that he went to confess her at La Bastide. Father Girard having persuaded her that there was

no crime in what had passed between them, she never so
much as mentioned it to her new director; but as she was
from time to time observed to be in perfect raptures about
the Jesuit, and twice or thrice endeavoured to run away by
night to meet him at Toulon, the Prior began to suspect
that something more than ordinary had been between
them, and that she was linked to her former confessor by
some secret charm.

'Upon this he began to probe Miss Cadiere's conscience,
who frankly owned to him the particulars above related,
and the whole that had passed between Father Girard and
her. He saw with astonishment that those things which had
till then been looked upon as wonders of Grace were only
delusions and tricks of the Devil; and nothing real in the
whole, but a horrible complication of shocking crimes . . .'

Upon hearing of this amazing reversal of interpretation,
the Bishop, who had been hitherto quite convinced that he
nurtured a Saint in his Diocese, examined Catharine
Cadiere himself and heard every word confirmed. He immediately announced his intention of destroying Girard
and of driving him out of the church. However, Catharine
herself intervened, begging the Bishop not to publish her
shame. Her entreaties were strengthened by the pleas of
her Dominican brother who beseeched the Bishop to spare
his family the shame and scandal that would inevitably
accrue to their name if the truth about his sister's relationship with Girard were made public. The Bishop relented,
and exorcized the unhappy Catharine.

Matters would have rested there had it not been for the
zealous concern of another Jesuit, Father de Sabatier who,
against all persuasion, charged Catharine's brother and
Father Nicholas with defaming Father Girard's character.
At the same time, he sent a posse of legal men to interro-
gate Catharine who, taken entirely by surprise but bound
by oath, made a full confession of her relationship with
Girard. This deposition, duly signed by Catharine Cadiere,
read as follows:

'18th November, 1730. Be it known to all men that Miss
Catharine Cadiere, daughter of the deceased M. Joseph
Cadiere, Merchant of Toulon, being sworn and having declared that she is of the age of one and twenty, deposes
that her first confessor was Mr. Giraud, Vicar of the
Cathedral Church of this city; that she was next directed by
Father Maurin, a bare-footed Carmelite, having a call to be
a nun of that order; but that the said Father Maurin, falling
into a tedious illness, she made choice of Father Sabatier,
the Jesuit, for her confessor, she being at that time between
fifteen and sixteen years old; that she went to the Jesuit
Convent to make a confession to Father Sabatier, but was
told that he was not yet recovered from his illness so as to
be able to receive it. This obliged the Deponent to take for
her director Mr. d'Oulonne, priest and lecturer of the Parish
of St. Louis, but he being very much taken up with the business of his parish, so that he often made her wait a long
time before he could hear her confession, her relations at
home scolded her for staying so long, because they wanted
her for the business of the shop and house, and sometimes
they even beat her for it. Her brother, Mr. Francis Cadiere,
an Ecclesiastic, being a student then in the Jesuit College,
told her of Father Girard, the Rector, who was from that
time her confessor for two years and an half.

'She had confessed to that Father about a year before
anything extraordinary happened, except that he inquired
into the deponent's circumstances, and who were her relations . . .

'Having inquired how she did after an intermitting fever
which had held her a fortnight, he kindly reproached her
for not sending to call him when she was ill. The deponent
answered that she was unwilling to give him so much
trouble, to which Father Girard replied, "You are a
simpleton. That is a trouble which I take with a great deal
of pleasure. Will you not for once give yourself to me?" Then
stooping down and putting his mouth close to hers, he
breathed very hard upon her, which made such a strange

impression in her mind that from that moment she felt a
violent passion and a strong inclination for the Father, and
told him at once that she gave herself up to him.

'The Deponent adds that for above six months before, he
had frequently said to her in the chair of confession, "Will
you not give yourself up to me? I know that the gracious God
requires something of you. He has great designs to accom-
plish upon you." And the deponent asking how he could
know that, the said Father Girard answered that he knew
it and had been sensible of it for a great while. From that
time he ordered her to receive the Sacrament every day,
but to do it in a different church that it might not be taken
notice of. From that time also she began to have frequent
visions which came upon her sometimes at church, sometimes at home, and sometimes in the street. These visions
consisted chiefly in seeing the celestial glory, and Heaven
opened with all the saints placed according to the several
degrees of glory to which they are raised . . .

'Having afterwards had several visions, sometimes of one
kind, sometimes of another, she always found the effect of
them was inflaming her passion for the said Father Girard,
who by her order came to see her every day, and sometimes
twice a day. When the Deponent said to him, "Is it possible,
Father, that I should have so great a passion for you, and
does the law of God produce such strange effects?" his
answer was that she should not be uneasy about that, for
his gracious God had united her to him . . .

'All the while she continued in this state, from first to last,
she was incapable of vocal prayer, and when she complained of this to Father Girard, he told her that it was not
necessary, to which the Deponent answered that she believed the saints had not walked in that way. Father Girard
told her that this was an extraordinary way, that we must
not always take the saints for our patterns, and that the
Lord had different ways of bringing such souls to himself.

'In another vision she saw a person in a state of mortal sin
and impurity, and being terrified by so dismal a sight, she

heard a voice which told her that if she had a mind to
deliver that soul from that miserable state in which she saw
it, she must submit to be possessed for a year. This she
communicated to Father Girard, her confessor, who, notwithstanding she showed the utmost aversion to it, forced
her to submit to be possessed. Immediately upon giving her
consent to it, she found herself possessed with a great
number of Devils which disordered her imagination and
took away her senses; nay, governed them so that in spite
of her they made her pronounce thousands of curses against
the saints, and blasphemies against the Eucharist, and all
our Sacred Mysteries ...

'When she was in the Confessional, Father Girard
ordered her to receive his breath, though she resisted it as
much as she could because the more he breathed on her the
more passionate and eager she was to embrace him ... Till
last Lent, Father Girard used to come every day to the
Deponent's house when she was in her fits of convulsion. He
went up to the second floor where she lay almost always in
bed, though sometimes she got up. He entered her chamber,
the door of which he locked on the inside, and as soon as
he sat down, her fits of convulsion became always more violent. She often found herself before him in indecent postures. Sometimes he made her sit down on the bed's foot
where he held her and pressed her to his bosom for two or
three hours together, kissing her face in a very amorous
manner very frequently, and almost every day that he
came ...

'She further deposes that in another vision she saw the
heart of Jesus Christ pierced with several wounds, and
heard a voice saying that it was wounded by the sins of
men and that as she was united to Jesus Christ she should,
by virtue of that union, participate in his wounds, which
she should perceive by a gash on her left side. And so it
actually happened to her, for that instant she felt a stroke
on that side where she found a wound which continued
open for three months without increasing or diminishing.

'Father Girard came every day to the Deponent's chamber, which he locked. Then he handled her neck and breasts, and sucked the wound ... She declares that when her health allowed her to go to the Jesuit Convent in Lent, one afternoon, Father Girard carried her into the church, where there was nobody but themselves, and that before he went into the chair of confession, he embraced and kissed her mouth ... She deposes further, that when Father Girard came to see her in her chamber and was locked up there with her, he frequently handled her private parts until she found herself all wet and sometimes swooned away. Not knowing what all this meant, she used to chide Father Girard about it, who only laughed at her.

'Having missed her periods for about three months, she acquainted Father Girard with it who, after that, frequently handled her belly, and for a week together made her take every day certain drugs of a reddish colour which caused an abortion. For eight days she lost a vast deal of blood with which there came away a lump of flesh. Having communicated this to Father Girard, he told her that it could not possibly be and that it was the Devil who had made her believe so.

'She adds further that one day, Father Girard made her strip to her shift upon the bed saying that he must punish her for her fault in not resigning herself, and that then she felt her private parts tickled and wet. At other times, he would lash her with his scourge and then kiss the places and that it was at those times that he used to tickle and wet her private parts. Also, one day while she was in the Monastery of St. Clare at Ollioules, there being nobody in the church but Father Girard and herself, he embraced her and kissed her, as he did frequently in the parlour, besides sucking her wound.'

Once this was done, the process of the law had been put in motion and hereafter the case became a confusing mixture of false evidence, recantation and intimidation. At the first hearing, witnesses were carefully selected by the Jesuits who

had continual access to the statements made by Girard's
accusers with the result that each witness for Girard made
statements which flatly contradicted those of the Cadiere
camp. Even more extraordinary, as soon as the proceedings
began Catharine was confined by law in the Ursuline Convent at Toulon, which was directed by the Jesuits. The
Mother Superior was herself a penitent of Girard's while
the lay sister assigned to Catharine was none other than the
daughter of one of Girard's penitents who had told
Catharine that he had committed similar offences with her.
As if this were not enough, direct action was taken to 'persuade' Catharine to recant.

'Miss Cadiere was obliged to attend the Bishop three
times in order to have a confessor appointed her, but could
obtain none except Mr. Berge, a beneficed clergyman, a
man wholly devoted to the Jesuits, as appears plainly from
the following passage. This priest comes to the Convent of
the Ursulines on the 31st of January last with pen, ink and
paper, attended by Father de Sabatier and two witnesses.
He goes into the parlour, sends for Miss Cadiere and tells
her he has come to receive her confession, but that she must
first make a formal recantation of what she had deposed
against Father Girard, and declare that it was all a calumny,
otherwise he could not confess her. And upon her answer-
ing that she was forced to make her complaint to the Officer
of the Justice, and had said nothing in it but the truth
which she could not retract, Mr. Berge walked off with
Father de Sabatier and the witnesses without hearing her
confession.'

This was indeed a terrible threat. Without confession,
Catharine would believe herself to be in a state of sin.
Psychologically it was a very clever move, for at that particular time she must have been in grave need of confession
to ease her mind and clear her conscience. Having failed
in this attempt, however, the Jesuits began to suborn
Catharine Cadiere's own witnesses. Although they met with
little real success this did have the effect of introducing

statements which considerably clouded the issue. The next move was more direct. Immediately before examination, the Ursulines persuaded Catharine to drink a glass of wine which, she later claimed, tasted strongly of salt. Thereafter she felt ill and, at the subsequent examination, which she was forced to attend, she made a complete recantation because she was in fear of her life. Further, she was confronted with no less than forty-six witnesses, including Girard, who insisted that nothing indecent had ever occurred between them, many of whom she had grave objections to but which she was not allowed to voice.

The only steadfast and incorruptible witnesses in this travesty of justice were the Abbess and Nuns of St. Clare who steadfastly refused to alter a single word of their evidence. Their insistence upon the truth of what they had seen presumably gave Catharine the necessary courage to carry on and she eventually reverted to her first statement. During the lengthy examination of the nuns of St. Clare, Catharine Cadiere was confined in a stinking cell at the Ursuline Convent. The room was bare but for a little mouldy straw, and she was handled very roughly by her 'jailers' who constantly threatened her with worse punishments if she did not recant. The examination of the inmates of St. Clare, however, considerably strengthened her case, since new evidence against Girard was revealed. As a result, she was moved to a convent at Aix and the entire matter was placed before the court in that town.

Throughout the case, Catharine Cadiere was treated as a criminal. She was confined in a series of convents which acted to all intents and purposes as jails. She was even denied confession, a measure granted to even the most hardened criminals. In the meantime, Father Girard moved about freely and, apart from having to answer a few embarrassing questions, which he was perfectly well equipped to deal with, he suffered no particular inconvenience.

The final outcome of the case was a simple and unsatisfactory compromise. Father Girard was acquitted in the

Civil Court of all charges brought against him but was delivered into the hands of the Ecclesiastical Courts who were expected to take whatever steps they thought necessary. Catharine Cadiere stood condemned of false evidence against a priest, but she was released from confinement and ordered to return to her mother in whose care she was legally placed.

This decision is a transparent compromise. So transparent, in fact, that justice can patently be seen not to have been done. There is, unfortunately, no record of what followed this decision, but it is surely obvious that the Ecclesiastical Court would take no action against Girard who had been effectively cleared in the Civil Court. Catharine, on the other hand, was publicly disgraced. The details of her relationship with Girard had been made public and even though the law said they were false, no one in Toulon was going to regard her now as a pious virgin. She had, in fact, been effectively undermined on all accounts. Perhaps as an indication that they knew what they were doing, the Court gave her the sop of her freedom which, in a small town bubbling over with scandal can scarcely have been preferable to prison to such a girl.

The church had won. The inviolability of the Jesuits had been established. The fact that it had been achieved by blatantly foul means did not matter. The authority of the church was re-affirmed, even though we can now see that such authority could act as a licence for all kinds of debauchery to men like Girard. The voice of a single innocent, even simple-minded, girl had been raised against the established authority and had been effectively quelled. The power she spoke against was too great. The stakes were too high. The man of God was exonerated, and the innocent was made to suffer.

It is no easy task, so long after the event, to arrive at a clear picture of the truth of the Cadiere Case. Much of it seems incomprehensible today, but we must always remember that many of the players in this drama, including Catharine Cadiere herself, were ignorant people, highly suggestible to the mystique of the church. The possibility of religious visions and revelations would strike them as miraculous, not silly. They would feel a genuine awe, bordering upon terror. Similarly, they believed in the Devil as strongly as they believed in God. If they slipped for a moment, they were in danger of falling into the Devil's clutches. Cases of such possession were rife at the time, and only the most exceptionally well-educated could even conceive of scoffing at such stories. Even so, today, this aspect of the case is by far the most puzzling.

Jean-Baptiste Girard's part in the proceedings is, on the contrary, relatively comprehensible. He was a man of hollow vows who evidently and beyond all doubt did not take his vow of celibacy with any seriousness. He was undoubtedly an ambitious man and, as far as the perversion of his office would allow, he was a womanizer. As we have already suggested, Catharine Cadiere was a ripe and perfect victim for his religio-sexual perversions. Even so, Girard did not lack willing partners among his female penitents. It was, no doubt, the suitability of her mind and situation, together with her extreme youth, which drew him to Catharine Cadiere. He was fifty, she was eighteen. She must have been a temptation indeed.

Most importantly, however, she had a reputation for amazing devoutness. This not only provided him with an opportunity to see her more frequently than would be usual, but also presented him with the possibility of making her a saint or, at the very least, a very respected religious figure. If things had not got out of hand, had Catharine been more, or perhaps less wily, he may well have succeeded. What more convenient way is there, after all, for disposing of an unwanted mistress than by renouncing her as a saint? The idea would surely appeal to any girl of suitable religious susceptibilities, and Girard himself would stand to gain the best of both the spiritual and the physical worlds.

All the evidence suggests that Catharine Cadiere was an extremely innocent girl. This may well have aided Girard in his plan. The idea of being selected by God for special service would not only appeal to her but could also disturb an untutored and emotional mind. His first embrace, the famous breathing upon her, could well have aroused purely feminine, physical impulses in her which might seem like a sort of spell or enchantment to a girl of this kind. She knew, after all, nothing of the world or of sex. Yet she must have been physically ready for a woman's experiences.

This attitude of mind, plus the fact that she was undoubtedly completely in Girard's power, both as a woman because she felt she loved him and as a penitent because he was her religious director, must have rendered her very receptive mentally. It would then be a comparatively easy task for Girard to suggest to her the substance of her visions, either verbally or by indicating certain passages she should read. Certainly the details of appropriateness of these visions suggest a more fertile and cunning imagination than Catharine's. At the same time, in her disturbed state, they would appear to be true to Catharine.

Once he had so arranged things that he was able to visit her alone in her room, it would be a relatively easy thing for him to suggest and even 'stage' new visions. By exciting her sexually, it would be quite possible for him to produce a state of mind and body which would accurately resemble a state of religious ecstasy. Similarly, since the supposedly divine voice is so explicit in its instructions, and since these instructions are invariably to Girard's advantage, it seems reasonable to suggest that, having produced a state of physical and mental excitement in his victim, he could then whisper the instructions which so aided his plan.

It is the matter of the stigmata, particularly the famous wound in Catharine Cadiere's side which, at first, seems the most inexplicable occurrence in the whole confusing affair. It seems certain that the wound was very real and not a figment of Catharine's imagination, since other witnesses also saw it. The clue to an explanation of this extraordinary happening lies in Girard's penchant for whipping, and in Catharine Cadiere's deposition. There can be no doubt that Girard did whip the girl, and his subsequent behaviour – the kissing of the inflamed buttocks and the sexual assault – would prove conclusively that his motive here was strictly sexual and not, as he presented it to the girl, punitive. Further, we know that Girard fabricated excuses in order to whip her. In other words, there is sufficient evidence in Girard's penchant for whipping as a sexual act to suggest that he was an avowed sadist.

In her deposition Catharine Cadiere claimed that she 'felt a stroke on that side' during her vision of the wounded heart, and that when she came out of her trance, there was indeed a wound in her flesh. If we accept that these trances were, at least at this stage in the relationship, induced by Girard by sexual or religious means, and bearing in mind his obvious sadism, might we not accept that Catharine did indeed feel 'a stroke', a blow or incision made with a knife by Girard himself? It is, after all, but a short step from flagellation to other forms of physical cruelty, and it is easily made if sexual pleasure is obtained as a result.

The wound had many advantages for Girard. Its miraculous appearance did much to bolster the myth of Catharine Cadiere's sanctity. It afforded him not only a valid reason for visiting her but also for undressing her in order to see and 'worship' the miraculous wound. However, it seems likely that his delight in 'sucking' the wound was sexual rather than reverent, a re-enactment of his initial act of sadism. Further, the making of the wound and his concern with it would also fit in with his religious calling. It is easy to make out a case for Girard as a lust-driven wolf in priest's clothing but this is altogether too simple. The Jesuits are extremely strict. To become a Jesuit priest was never easy, and they were usually chosen for the fierceness of their fervour and the depth of their devotion. Certainly Girard expressed little of these qualities in his relationship with Catharine Cadiere, or did he?

He was a man of fifty. There cannot have been many years in which he was at liberty to indulge his worldly tastes, for preferment in a Jesuit order is a long, slow process. In this time he must have been imbued with a great deal of the mystique of the church, for to suggest anything else would be to deny its obvious power. But if he was, in fact, a sadist forced to celibacy for long periods, would it not be reasonable to suggest his attraction to Catharine Cadiere comprised not only his professional ambition and his animal lust, but also the elements of a grandiose devotion and a terrible sadism? There could easily have been a religious significance, a terrible but magnificent ecstasy in his providing Catharine with replicas of the Saviour's wounds. In the infliction of this at once real and symbolic pain, he would be fulfilling both his spirit and his flesh.

The most convincing explanation for Girard's behaviour is that he was a religious fanatic and a sexual maniac – a formidable combination which could exist and even flourish undetected in the rarefied atmosphere of the church of the time, until temptation in the shape of Catharine Cadiere appeared.

Once the case came out into the open, Girard had to do little to defend himself. The Jesuits, and through them, the entire church rallied to his support. He had prudently obtained all the incriminating letters he had written to Catharine and throughout the proceedings he refused to produce them, claiming that they contained material vouchsafed to him by Catharine under the conditions of the confessional. Despite Catharine's insistence that he might produce them, that there was nothing left to her that might not be made public, he remained bound by his oath – or so he claimed. It is doubtful, however, if they would have materially altered the course of the case. The Jesuits were simply too powerful for any but the most radically progressive court to accept Catharine's testimony without hesitation. As a result, the very cloak of inviolability under which he had perpetrated his horrifying crimes also protected him from just punishment. And when one considers that in all probability the church was protecting a sadistic maniac, it is not surprising that it, and particularly the Jesuits, have since fallen to a much less exalted status.

But what of the other protagonist in the case, the innocent victim of Girard's sexual sadism and religious mysticism? When all the evidence is considered, Catharine Cadiere remains an ambivalent figure. Today it seems impossible that any girl could be quite so innocent, yet given the conditions of the time and society in which she lived, it is not impossible. However, Catharine Cadiere, for all her innocence, took part in a surprising number of decidedly non-innocent activities for a long time and without complaint. It is, after all, remarkable that she never once willingly complained of Girard's behaviour. She almost certainly was innocent at the beginning of their liaison, but she quickly learned a great many things which must surely have seemed shocking and immodest to a truly innocent girl.

On purely religious grounds, there is much that is surprising and difficult to believe in Catharine Cadiere's statements. Since she was obviously an unusually devout girl, one who at a very early age had seriously considered taking the veil, she complied with extraordinary ease to suggestions of Girard's that she surely must have known were contrary to all the canons of the Roman Church. Her very sincere faith suggests that her knowledge of the church and its forms would be considerable. It seems, therefore, highly unlikely that she would so unquestioningly believe Girard's extraordinary statement that vocal prayer was not essential. She must have known that, according to the precepts of the church, the only way to God was through mortification of the body and the exaltation of the spirit. She could not consent to be joined to Girard in this overtly physical way and still have truly believed that she was a good Catholic.

Much is explained, of course, by the fact that she, a susceptible, unworldly girl, was head over heels in love with her confessor. Indeed, her insistence on telling him of her doubts, e.g., about vocal prayer, bear witness to her innocence and concern with the state of her soul and conscience. But even the most extraordinary passion would scarcely have blinded her to the very blatant misdirections of her priest. Even if she were very corrupt, which it seems she was not, no girl of her upbringing and previous piety would have consented so easily to be possessed by the Devil. That is too much even for God to ask, for it could place her in a state of mortal sin, and would require her to overcome a very real and definable fear of the unknown based on centuries of myth and teaching. She certainly could not have agreed to be possessed and still retain her spiritual innocence unless, of course, she knew that she was only pretending.

Similarly, given the fact of her modesty, which would be natural in a girl of her age and station, and which is borne out not only by the piety of her life but by her rejection of several honourable proposals of marriage, it is very difficult to believe that such a girl could frequently have her sexual parts caressed and kissed and still remain innocent. A truly modest girl would still try to prevent any man from taking such overtly sexual liberties, yet Catharine Cadiere never complained or spoke of these matters. She insisted always that she did not know what these caresses meant, but she never suggests that Girard used force on those occasions. It is not the act of a modest girl to allow a man to finger her vagina, even if she is unaware of its sexual significance.

It would seem much nearer the truth, therefore, that once she had fallen, as she undoubtedly did, hopelessly in love with Girard, Catharine Cadiere became a willing partner in the events which followed. Since she loved him as a man and respected him as a priest, she was eminently suggestible. It would surely have been an easy task for him to persuade her to aid him in the myth of her sanctity, for this would give them an opportunity to be together without interruption. She would surely yield to the pleas of a man she avowedly loved, and would herself wish to see him at every available opportunity. Under his direction it would be easy for her to simulate the divine trances and convulsions which would enable him to lock himself up in her room for long periods. On all points it seems much more likely that Catharine intrigued with Girard to gain time to consummate their affair.

Because she was religious and susceptible, perhaps Girard succeeded in drawing her into his religio-sadistic fantasy. Or did the whippings and the woundings come as a complete surprise to her? Unless she was an avowed masochist, which would be a remarkable coincidence, it seems likely that she did, at least in some measure, agree to his demands. If not, surely even one in love would have complained at receiving such barbarous treatment. If she did not share his fantasy, it is more than possible that Girard justified the physical abuse which she suffered at his hands as a penance to God for the sin she was committing in having an affair with a priest. If this is the case, then Catharine Cadiere can make little justifiable claim to innocence, although there are extenuating circumstances in her case.

If these suppositions are true, Catharine Cadiere's detailed deposition must contain only a version of the truth. It is important to remember, however, that she did not willingly accuse Girard. She was undoubtedly frightened by the admission she made to Father Nicholas. But at that time, she obviously thought that Girard had thrown her over. The intervention of the Bishop would have revealed Girard's plan to send her away and his last letter, declining any longer to be her confessor, was a cold and chilly composition. She must have felt very alone, and the need to confess must have been great. The astuteness of Father Nicholas undoubtedly revealed more than she meant to say, but then, if her lover had forsaken her, what better course was open

to her than to make a full confession and seek consolation
in the church? The august presence of the Bishop himself
would certainly be sufficient to draw a full confession from
her. She had already tried to see Girard, presumably to beg
him to stay with her. After her confession, she beseeched
the Bishop to take no action against Girard.

Therefore, although Catharine Cadiere's deposition is
probably only partially true, it was not made in revenge.
This is decidedly not the action of a woman scorned. Once
the matter had come to the attention of Father Nicholas
and the Bishop, and there can be no doubt that it did so
accidentally, Catharine was unable to tell the full truth
unless she was prepared to condemn herself out of her own
mouth. In the absence of her lover who was now obviously
finished with her, her only conceivable consolation was the
church. Alone, her sins must have weighed heavily upon
her. Thus, faced with the necessity of making a legal statement, she simply told what had happened while stressing
her own innocence and excusing her behaviour by claiming
that she was enchanted and possessed. To have told the un-
varnished truth, if indeed she was a willing partner in
Girard's debaucheries, would have been to invite the full
wrath of both the church and the law.

As it was, Catharine Cadiere suffered far more than her
lover, who undoubtedly remains the more guilty of the two.
She had gained little joy from her love. She had suffered
physically, had become pregnant and been aborted, she was
imprisoned, threatened and cruelly treated. She ended up
the subject of public scandal. At the end of the case she had
little hope of making a marriage and even less of being
regarded as a devout, pious woman. Even the convents
would think twice before admitting her, if her experiences
within those sacred walls had not already utterly disen-
chanted her. Above all, she was a girl who had nearly become a saint. Given her natural piety this must have meant
something very great to her. At the end, she had farther to
fall, and fewer illusions to sustain her.

The Cadiere case is a remarkable example of the iniqui- ties not only of the church but of any power-structure which becomes, through lack of counter-authority, a law unto itself. As a result, justice is stifled and the innocent or, in this case, the less guilty, are persecuted. The crimes com- mitted by Girard are moral, ecclesiastical and civil, while those committed by Catharine Cadiere are the result of foolishness. Yet the church, of which she was a devout member, had no refuge for her. It was concerned solely to protect its own image and its own ministers. Yet it would be an error to place the blame solely at the door of the church. If it was guilty of erecting a framework which was ripe for misuse, it took a man of Girard's unquestioned villainy to exploit it. Yet that very system shielded him and, by so doing, condoned his actions.